By Mabel Farnum

STREET
of the
HALF-MOON

An Account of the Spanish Noble,
PEDRO CLAVER

THE BRUCE PUBLISHING COMPANY
MILWAUKEE

Nihil obstat: EDWARD G. MURRAY, D.D., Censor librorum
Imprimatur: ✠ WILLIAM CARDINAL O'CONNELL, Archbishop of Boston
July 29, 1940

TO THE BELOVED LITTLE COMMUNITY AT SAN PEDRO CLAVER, CARTAGENA, COLOMBIA, S. A., WHO GUARD THE PRECIOUS RELICS OF THE SLAVE OF THE SLAVES.

FATHER ANTONIO PINILLA, S.J., SUPERIOR
FATHER MARCO RESTREPO, S.J.
FATHER MARTIN NUÑEZ, S.J.
FATHER ÁNGEL MURUZÁBAL, S.J.
FATHER AURELIANO BUSTOS LARA, S.J.

BROTHER FRANCISCO VÁRQUEZ, S.J.
BROTHER CARLOS GAVIRIA, S.J.
BROTHER JOSÉ DE JESÙS GOMEZ, S.J.

AND

BROTHER HILARIO PEREDA, S.J., WHO WENT TO JOIN SAINT PETER CLAVER IN HEAVEN SHORTLY AFTER HE HAD BEGUN TO PRAY FOR THIS BOOK.

Acknowledgments

IN THE preparation of *Street of the Half-Moon*, the principal works consulted in relation to the Apostle himself were *La Vie du Vénérable Père Pierre Claver De La Compagnie De Jesus*, by Père Bertrand-Gabriel Fleuriau, S.J., published at Paris in 1751; the *Vida de San Pedro Claver*, by the Reverend Pedro Adan Brioschi (Archbishop Brioschi), published in the same city in 1889; *San Pedro Claver De La Compagnia De Jesùs*, by Father Manuel Mejia, S.J., published at Cartagena, Colombia, in 1918; also numerous early Spanish books, newspapers, and documents. All these were found to be in perfect agreement as to the spirit and apostolate of the Saint.

Through the generous and painstaking offices of Father Aureliano Bustos Lara, S.J., of San Pedro Claver in Cartagena, much data never previously printed is included in this book. Father Bustos also supplied the author with journals, maps, charts, photographs, and printed accounts, the latter including *Cartagena y sus Cercanias*, by José P. Urueta, with additions and annotations by Eduardo De Piñeres; the work, in four volumes, by Dr. Camilo Delgado, *Historias, Leyendas y Tradiciones de Cartagena*, and the special edition of *El Mercurio*, published at Cartagena, in December, 1933, to mark the fourth centenary of the founding of the city.

By means of frequent letters flown across the Caribbean, Father Bustos instructed the author in the topography and history of the seventeenth-century city and helped her to acquire a better knowledge of the language and people. This invaluable assistance embraced the establishing of the exact routes and spots which the Apostle daily followed and visited in his heroic labors of spiritual and corporal mercy.

For the history of New Granada (the Colombia of today) the following authors were consulted: Jesùs Maria Henao and Gerardo Arrubla (*Historia de Colombia*), Phanor Elder, J. Levine, R. B. Cunninghame Graham, and Blair Niles. The publications of the Pan-American Union at Washington, D. C., were also found helpful.

The data on the origins and progress of the slave trade was obtained from old manuscripts composed by sea captains, contemporary writers, travelers, and others who visited the slave coasts of Africa at a time when the slave traffic had been well established. A singularly happy agreement on the part of these authors points to the truth and accuracy of their statements.

In regard to the local coloring of the book much was gathered firsthand by the author from what still remains to be studied in our day.

In its general aspects the Cartagena of the present is the Cartagena of St. Peter Claver. However, in the seventeenth century there were dense forests in certain parts of the city; these have long since disappeared, making way for the dwellings of the people and for business establishments. The Calle de la Media Luna is today largely a commercial thoroughfare; in the time of the Apostle it was a street of lovely old Spanish houses.

The church of San Pedro Claver, formerly San Ignacio, enshrines the mortal remains of the self-sacrificing and courageous Claver. The narrow street on which it fronted in his day has since been converted into a small square. In the venerable College and Residencia adjoining it a valiant little Community of spiritual brothers of the Saint are carrying on a most fruitful apostolate to the Negroes whose cause was so dear to St. Peter's loving and childlike heart.

The name, Cartagena of the Indies, was used in colonial times to distinguish the city of the Caribbean from Cartagena in Spain.

To all who helped me in the remote or immediate preparation of this book my gratitude and appreciation are extended. To:

His Eminence, William Cardinal O'Connell, Archbishop of Boston, whose distinguished gifts and apostolic works, and whose fatherly interest in my literary efforts since my sixteenth year have blessed and inspired me to persevere in the apostolate of the pen.

Most Reverend Pedro Adan Brioschi, Archbishop of Cartagena, for the inspiration of his beautiful *Vida* and for the priceless gift of a first-class relic of the Apostle.

Most Reverend Richard J. Cushing, LL.D., Auxiliary Bishop of Boston and Director of the Propagation of the Faith Society for that Archdiocese, who published my recent book on Xavier, *A Carrack Sailed Away,* and whose zealous encouragement and direction are largely responsible for the publication of the present work.

Rev. Joseph J. Husslein, S.J., of St. Louis University, for his scholarly criticism and aid in the revision of the manuscript.

Rev. Aureliano Bustos Lara, S.J., of San Pedro Claver, Cartagena, Colombia, S. A., my collaborator in the task of gathering the data on St. Peter Claver, his adopted country and his times.

J. Keetch Ludewig, Chief Engineer of Economics of the Pan American Union, who furnished me with valuable books, magazines, and photographs on Colombia.

José Mayo, of the United Fruit steamship *Chiriqui,* who accompanied me on my two visits to San Pedro Claver in Cartagena and introduced me to the spiritual brothers of the Saint.

Significantly, some of the warmest tributes to the Apostle of the Negroes have come from persons not of the Faith, who visited the scenes in which Claver lived and worked and familiarized themselves with his history. Of these none is more eloquent than that of J. B. Cunninghame Graham in his *Cartagena and the Banks of the Sinú,* published in London in 1920. Characterizing Claver as a Saint "humble and self-denying and devoid of pride," this noted author and traveler adds:

"It pleases me to think that his self-sacrifice and life of toil amongst the Negroes was not unrecognized. . . . In 1851 Pius IX beatified the Saint of Cartagena, and, as with such a man the arguments of the *Advocatus Diaboli* could not have been convincing, his canonization followed, in 1888, under Pope Leo XIII.

"Long before that, the inhabitants of the *'Noble y Leal Cuidad'* — the noble and loyal town — had enshrined him in their hearts."

Preface by the General Editor

FEW scenes have power so deeply to arouse the imagination as that of Peter Claver standing on the wharf of Cartagena and eagerly awaiting the arrival of the latest slave ship. With straining eyes he watches the broad hulk heaving into sight, but his thoughts are with the human cargo, the living chained to the dead, and both tossed together with each jolt of the boat, in their black hold of horrors.

Behind him, in languorous beauty, untroubled by thoughts of compassion, lies the colorful city, its wealth and nobility most brilliantly displayed in the Calle de la Media Luna, the Street of the Half-Moon.

Here, but just now, Claver had stood before the flowering balconies of the old aristocratic mansions, a pathetic figure in frayed cloak, basket in hand, begging with eyes downcast for gifts of fruit and medicine, salves and refreshing drinks and delicacies of whatever kind for the lacerated, striped, and tortured creatures whom he would be the only one to welcome with a touch of human love. But he was not a man to be denied the favor he so humbly asked, and from their lace-hung lookouts the bright ladies hurriedly sent down their servants with dainties from their tables.

What follows in this book is the account, strictly historical in every detail, of the wonderful life of this most marvelous man. A dramatic biography it is, with enlivening dialogue, vivid narration, rich coloring and picturesque background such as of all cities in its day could be offered by Cartagena of the Indies, radiant queen of the blue Caribbean.

But, lest the easy flow of language prove deceptive, it is well to admit the reader into some of the author's personal intimacies regarding the making of this volume.

Little has been known by writers, for now many generations, of the fertile region lying about the Magdalena River, the warm coastal section of Colombia in which Cartagena is situated. Non-Catholic artists and authors, it is true, have visited the place and fallen in love with its beauty, but nothing has specifically been told us of the surroundings amid which the Saint himself lived and of the customs of the people that have changed but slightly since his day.

Before, therefore, paying her own personal visit of devotion and research to the country where Claver lived and worked and prayed, the author spent months of preliminary study in reviewing the literature supplied from such authoritative sources as the Pan American Union, the National Geographic Society, and similar fountain heads. The voyage itself to Colombia afforded an opportunity to learn much from fellow travelers, natives of that land.

But the author's supreme good fortune was to meet in Cartagena itself with a spiritual brother of the Saint, a member of the Community which has taken the place of that in which Claver lived, the Reverend Aureliano Bustos Lara, S.J., then connected with the Church named after the great Apostle of the Negroes and replacing that in which he heard the confessions of the slaves. Not merely could he guide the author over the paths that Claver had trod, but he entered into a systematic correspondence with her that regularly supplied her thereafter with pertinent information and all local items.

But more than that was required to make the past live again. From the principal emporium in the Saint's own city, as well as from the ever-dependable Father Bustos, now came to her large shipments of old, yellowed books and papers, tattered, curious, and precious. Among them were ancient prints and invaluable maps that made it possible to plot out the exact location of many points important in the story of the Saint. And beyond all expectation, there was included a picture and description of the *cumbia,* the superstitious dance of the African slaves so powerfully described in these pages, as well as a minute account of that masterpiece of engineering skill, to which no reference could be found in other literature, the Great Wall of Cartagena on which multitudes of slaves were engaged in Claver's day.

These hints will suffice to make understandable the author's protestation that there is "not one guess" in this book — not even as to the color of a flower or the plumage of a tropical bird, or the gentle winsomeness of that dearest friend and helper of the Saint, who occupies so large a place in this narrative, Doña Isabel d'Urbina.

"I am sure," the author ventured to say, "there is not one guess in that book. I was completely honest in doing it, even though I knew that only the d'Urbina family up in heaven, and a few others would know the truth of it. Nothing is guesswork." What could not be proved to a nicety was relinquished from the picture.

That is the reader's voucher, and a splendid one it is, worthy of the best modern hagiography.

True, recourse was had to the use of dialogue in places where this was of service as an admirable medium to throw revealing side lights on the Saint, to convey a realization of the popular estimate of him by the slaves or by their wealthy and often purely commercial owners, and finally, to acquaint the reader in a pleasant way with historic backgrounds. Similarly, while all the characters of this narrative are entirely historical, we have as accessories or supernumeraries one cloth merchant and two or three slaves. These are no more than stage appurtenances, as we may say, to the great central drama that is enacted in this book.

That drama, to use the words of the author's subtitle, is "An Account of the Spanish Noble, Pedro Claver" — the noble who became a Jesuit, an Apostle of the Negro slaves, and who solemnly vowed before God to devote all his life to them in Cartagena of the Indies. Nothing regarding him that has been introduced into this book is in the slightest degree fictitious.

We may, therefore, venture to say that here we have the first living representation of St. Peter Claver, *seen in his own setting and atmosphere.*

And might we not add that this corresponds precisely with the method set forth by Saint Ignatius in the "contemplations" prescribed in his *Spiritual Exercises?* Of special importance at their beginning is always "the composition of place," the background work so carefully done in the present book. With the scene of action vividly impressed on our mind, the great founder, whose spiritual son St. Peter Claver rejoiced to be, confidently leads us on to a study of the "persons, words, and acts," after the necessary preparatory prayer, and finally reaches the height of realization in asking us to participate personally in the events repeated before the eyes of our imagination. Thus in the contemplation of the Nativity he bids us see our Lady and St. Joseph and the Infant Jesus, after His birth, "looking at and contemplating them and *tending them* in their necessities as though I were present, with all possible homage and reverence." And, as it were, to set us a practical example in this he introduces also "the servant maid." She is an accessory in the scene.

But particularly pertinent as illustrating the importance of background work are the directions given by this divinely instructed spiritual director for "the second prelude" to the same contemplation of the Nativity, "seeing the spot," as he says:

"It will be here to see with the eyes of the imagination the road from Nazareth to Bethlehem; considering its length, breadth, and whether the way be level or through valleys and over hills; and likewise seeing the spot or cave of the Nativity, how large or small, how low or high, and how it is prepared."

The method insisted upon by this "heavenly Patron of all spiritual exercises," as St. Ignatius was declared to be in the Apostolic Constitution *Summorum Pontificum* of July 25, 1922, is the method consistently employed throughout this book. It makes visible with minute accuracy the setting of every action, not merely as a literary technique, such as it rightfully is, but to draw souls more closely to feel the beauty of holiness as illustrated in St. Peter Claver.

As a related purpose, it is the author's desire to serve, without harangue or propaganda, the Negro cause. We have happily passed the Cartagena period, we have surmounted the *Uncle Tom's Cabin* stage, but we need a book that will help us to face in the proper spirit the further adjustment of the Negro's place in our civilization.

Attention, too, should be called to the effort here made to arrange in true chronological sequence the events that have never been assigned to any definite period in the Saint's career. In too many instances earlier biographers were content with stringing together such happenings, like beads upon a chain. This made it exceedingly difficult to recover the clues to a correct order of time. Bravely and with no little success the author attacked this problem. Not all events, it may be added, could be included in this book. A wise selection was imperative.

So, in a new life, based on new research, we are privileged to follow San Pedro Claver in his old familiar surroundings and amid the friends most close to him. If his eagerness for personal penance may at times overawe us, we must remember that it was the excess of love for Christ which made him find in this a relief for his great ardor by suffering with the Christ who died for him.

JOSEPH HUSSLEIN, S.J., PH.D.,
General Editor,
Science and Culture Series.

St. Louis University,
February 5, 1940.

Part I

Sunrise Over the Caribbean

Chapter I

AT THE window of his chamber overlooking the curling waters of the Caribbean, stood Father Pedro Claver, scanning with anxious eye the far horizon. The sun had not yet risen, but the light of dawn was breaking over Cartagena of the Indies.

A galleon was expected any day now from the shores of Africa, with its cargo of negro slaves, destined to be sold into lifelong bondage under cruel masters.

Across that wide expanse of steel-gray waters a Spanish conquistador, Don Pedro Heredia, had voyaged more than eight decades before to take possession of a new kingdom for his sovereign, Philip II. After him others had followed, but for the most part intent upon purposes of far different kind.

One, in particular, had left an unhallowed memory. He was the pirate Drake, whose frigate hove in sight of the noble city on Ash Wednesday of the year 1586. With twenty ships and twenty-three hundred men the restless adventurer from London sacked and despoiled Cartagena. Not satisfied with this act of vandalism, he exacted a sum of four hundred thousand ducats as a reward for refraining from burning it to the ground. Only the courage of Bishop Juan de Montalvo influenced the marauder to lessen his demands. He finally deigned to accept the amount of one hundred seven thousand ducats, together with an abandoned convent which he utilized as a temporary dwelling place for his followers. He had already burned most of the houses in Getsemani, a section of the city extending a little over one thousand meters, and caused all the church bells to be converted into artillery.

Those tragic times were now past and Cartagena was enjoying peace within her borders. But a far greater tragedy engrossed the heart and mind of the young Religious from Catalonia. It was the spiritual destitution of thousands of negro slaves brought to those shores.

Father Pedro's cell was small and close. Its furnishings were scant. A rough hide, spread out upon the floor in a corner of the tiny room, served him for a bed. In addition there were two wooden seats, a stool and a table. On the latter lay the priest's breviary and two volumes of Cases of Conscience. Conspicuous against the wall hung a crucifix, crudely colored. On one side of it might be seen a picture of the Redeemer at the column of flagellation; on the other, a likeness of St. Peter weeping over his denial of the Lord.

The young Jesuit was a man of mortification as well as of prayer. The cloak thrown across his bed of hide was frayed and soiled, but it served a magnificent purpose since it could readily be converted into a mantle for the aged and sick slaves. His habit, too, was sadly worn and faded, but he did not wish a new one. No doubt it fitted best the surroundings amid which he labored.

To the ears of the ardent Apostle came the sound of restless waves lapping against the low stone wall that formed the boundary of the narrow garden below. At that slight distance it was no louder than the hum of the brightly plumaged cocinera, boring into the painted hearts of the flowers. Little spiral clouds were anchored in the sky, that in the tropics always seems an immense distance from the earth. These somewhat relieved the brilliance of land and sea. Save for the creaking of the ox-drawn cart, hauling huge blocks of granite to an unfinished section of the great wall of Cartagena, the old city of Don Pedro Heredia lay quite still below him.

Father Pedro was in a reflective mood, recalling events and scenes of his early life, a life as yet comprised within the short span of twenty-six years.

From his good parents, particularly from a holy mother, he had learned of the singular providence of God exercised from the first in his behalf.

Remarkable for faith and piety were both his parents, Don Pedro Claver and Ana Sabocana, and both equally were of noble lineage. The young Pedro, himself, born several years after the marriage of the couple, was the fruit of fervent prayer.

"Pedro," Doña Ana had said to her husband, "if God will give us a child I am ready to dedicate it to His service, that so He may answer our prayers."

"If God gives us a son," Don Pedro promptly replied, "the child shall be His before being ours. He shall be the welcome Owner. And if God calls him to His service I shall bless His Holy Will."

Father Pedro Claver most lovingly recalled the sentiment expressed by Ana Sabocana as she made her sacrificial offering. Often in later days his noble father repeated her words to him that the boy might never forget them.

"By the name I bear," Doña Ana had said, "I trust that our prayers will reach the Throne of the Almighty. Anna, the mother of Samuel; Anna, the Mother of Mary, made the sacrifice of their offspring. Since you consent, my dear Pedro, I shall consider myself happy to imitate those holy women."

Such faith and submission were not to go unrewarded. She had made her bargain with God, and God accepted it.

Soon the worthy couple rejoiced in the birth of their little son whom they named "Pedro."

The young Religious vividly remembered the prayers he had been wont to recite at the knees of his saintly mother, and on going to the Novitiate at Tarragona, taking with him a few of his childhood's treasures: little crosses, statues and pictures of our Lord and our Lady. As a mere boy he had made use of them in teaching his companions the truths of their holy Faith. This zeal had grown within him during his college days at Barcelona, under the direction of the Jesuits, and with God's grace had fructified into his vocation. On August 7, 1602, he entered the Society of Jesus.

Most deeply impressed upon his mind of all his novitiate experiences was the memory of his pilgrimage to Montserrat. With two novice companions, he begged his way from town to town. Eagerly he bore the burden of the hardships when courage failed the others. At last, gleaming on its hilltop across the green valley, they saw the shrine of Montserrat. It was the spot sacred to every son of the Society of Jesus, where the impress of the holy feet of their Founder had hallowed the very rocks and stones. Falling on his knees, the youthful novice prayed to the Soldier Saint of Loyola to obtain for him the grace that he might worthily consummate his course in the Company of Jesus, and tenderly he turned to our Lady to bless his sublime adventure.

After the completion of the two prescribed years of novitiate, Claver took his first vows.

A teaching experience at the Jesuit College of Girona now followed, whence he passed on to the newly founded College of Majorca for the study of philosophy.

Here began one of the world's greatest and most holy friendships, which was to leave a profound imprint upon all his life. At Majorca the young religious met for the first time the saintly old lay brother, Alfonso Rodriguez, then holding the humble post of porter at the College.

Alfonso pointed out to Pedro the needs of the missions and inspired him with zeal for a missionary career.

While still at Majorca, Claver applied for the American missions. Two years later, on the completion of his course in theology, his petition was granted. And so, in April of the year 1610, the young religious set sail for the New World.

He and his companions started on their journey with but little luggage: the rule book, crucifix, a single change of garments, a biretta, and a cloak.

On shipboard the ardent young missionary exercised his first real apostolate among the sick and needy. To those in want of food he carried all he could beg, serving them as a brother. Because of his noble origin he was seated at the captain's table; this privilege enabled him to convey the choicest portions of his own food to the sick.

The ship carried one hundred and fifty in crew besides a few soldiers. As the men were free from duty for a brief period, Claver gathered them about him and counseled and prayed with them. The delightful simplicity and candor of the young noble made a most favorable impression on these rude men. In their regard for their teacher and their respect for his counsels they were soon reciting the rosary in common and performing other exercises of piety.

Even the officers, whose worst fault was a propensity to indulge in indecent language, soon ceased to use it in Claver's presence and many ceased to use it at all.

The missionaries sailing with Claver were aware of the holiness of their companion. They said to one another: "It is well he is with us, for God will protect the ship which carries so beautiful a soul."

On the morning of his arrival in the Indies, Cartagena

had arisen, like a bride, from the sea. Amber and violet-colored mists hung over her yellow sands, her moss-covered fortresses, her white domes and turrets, and the finished sections of the great walls, so soon to swallow up a chosen soul, never again to let him free.

Quickly Pedro Claver had run forward to the shore. Forgetting everything save the fact that he had at last reached the scene of his chosen labors, he knelt and kissed the ground. Tears welled in his deep eyes as he prayed to thank God for the wonderful favor bestowed on him, to pledge his loyal and devoted service, and to ask for all the strength that he would need to carry out his sacrifice.

In the little damp house of the Jesuit Fathers, Pedro Claver found conditions far other than he had pictured them. For when, weary after the hard voyage, he threw himself on his hard bed, it was not to sleep. True, the public slaughterhouse near by was closed for the night. But adjacent to it were several drinking places that kept open house. The profane songs drifting up from these places, as the night revellers indulged in an orgy of pleasure, aroused in the young religious mingled feelings of pity and indignation.

Soon, despite his longing to remain in Cartagena, he was ordered to Santa Fe de Bogotá, in the mountains of the interior, to continue his studies.

Up the tortuous Magdalena River he started out in an enormous raft called a champan. The journey was difficult, monotonous and filled with hardships. Again it was young Claver who encouraged his companions and revived their enthusiasm.

In the city of the gallant Quesada, who had erected the first church in Bogota and built twelve huts about it, naming them for the Twelve Apostles, Claver filled the dual role of student and missionary. In the narrow lanes and wide market place he found many souls to whom he could speak a word of friendly counsel and cheer. The streets of Bogota were very quiet, for the hempen sandals tramping to and fro made no sound. He loved best to walk through the Calle de la Agonia, Street of Our Saviour's Agony, and meditate on the Via Dolorosa of his Divine Lord.

However happy he was in his life of prayer and action, Claver had awaited the call to return to Cartagena with the utmost yearning. As he looked beyond the glistening domes of the monasteries with their grilled enclosures and radiant flower beds, his soul traveled out across the grassy *sabaña*, down the River Magdalena, to the old walled-in city of his choice.

At last the supreme call had come. Back to the Queen of the Caribes! Back to remain forever! Just one year more, and he was to receive the priceless favor of the priesthood and in the little Chapel of Our Lady was to offer up for the first time the holy Sacrifice of the Mass.

Here, then, was Pedro Claver now, in the Carthage of his choice.

Taking up the worn cloak from the bed of hide, and casting one more glance toward the image of the Crucified, Claver turned and went forth to begin a hard day's work for his negro slaves.

Chapter II

UP THE winding channel of the Bay of Cartagena where pelicans fluttered in the sunlight; past Boca Chica, its "Great Mouth," and beyond the grim bastions along the walls, a lilac haze came floating into the old city, there to take on added radiance from the flowering bushes and brightly tinted walls of the houses.

Bells were pealing from the tower of the Convent of Santa Clara to the northeast of the city. Here Doña Catalina Cabrera, foundress of the house, and her three sisters in religion, had been cloistered now for two years. At the same time, up from the eastern shores of the Caribbean, past the cathedral and the Palace of the Inquisition, rose the tuneful notes of Carmel. In the Calle de Estrada, Street of the Star, all sounds met and blended. So the prayers of the daughters of Santa Teresa of Avila were joined to those of the daughters of Santa Clara for all the souls in Cartagena and the great world beyond.

Outside the old slave warehouse near the foot of the Calle de San Ignacio, the Caribbean stroked the glistening sands as gently as a Spanish mother might caress her child. Yet beneath the semblance of peace lurked a strain of willfulness. Unleashed, it had lured to their doom many brave ships. Now only the dark fin of a shark, protruding from the jade-colored waves, broke the tranquility of the vast expanse.

None of the brightness of earth and sun, however, penetrated the old warehouse where Claver stood in the midst of his spiritual children. To his sensitive, priestly ears came the sound of jumbled voices in many tongues, rising from the groups around him. Now it resembled the chattering of the red monkeys that swung from the great trees in the forests; again, the melancholy whine of the sloth. To the eyes that had loved to look upon the beauties of nature, strange and disconcerting pictures were presented: bodies oddly misshapen, limbs distorted, faces swollen and blotched, often hideous in expression.

Until Father Pedro had come into their midst these Negroes had been like dumb creatures shut away in a wilderness where the sun's rays never penetrated. On the bodies of their sick and aged the skin had turned lifeless like wrinkled parchment. Now with tenderest care the Father stooped to bathe and anoint their ulcerous sores.

For his labors on behalf of the unfortunate slaves he was bitterly disliked by the majority of the slave owners. This he well knew, but it caused him no concern. His interest was in the spiritual welfare of the slaves, without forgetting their temporal needs.

Unbelievable were the sufferings these slaves had endured before they were sold into the bondage of their present heartless masters.

Only the previous day Claver had listened to the recital of a tale of horrid woe and injustice that had come to him from the lips of a runaway Negro, a slave on an estate situated a short distance from Cartagena.

Living in his tiny hut on the Slave Coast, beneath the shade trees for which the region was noted, the man's early life had been bright and joyous in this favored spot of the most fertile soil in all Africa. The country around had resembled a vast garden where, after each year's careful sowing, the crops sprang up to wave in the amber sunshine. Giant hedges enclosed the entire village, and from the hills about the natives beheld an enchanting vista of the sea.

Then — one terrible night — all that world had come to an end for him.

He had gone alone down the footpath leading from his home to a well, a short distance away, to draw water for his sick child. Suddenly, the pail was knocked from his hand and a heavy blow on the head sent him reeling into a swoon.

When he regained consciousness he was astounded to find that a cold breeze was blowing on his naked body — his captors had torn off his cotton garments and divided them among themselves. He was lying on the deck of a slave trader bound for New Granada in the Indies. Already his masters were preparing to push him, and the stricken group of fellow captives around him, down into the filthy hold.

Soon the ship's deck was empty and, sulkily, the great monster of the sea continued to plough her way through the swirling black waters, bearing onward to lasting servitude her sorrowful cargo.

Vanished forever the ties of a simple contented home life; vanished wife and children, the little cottage under the trees, the familiar pastoral scenes. The unhappy man was chained to five others. Not far from him, in another group, was a dead man, shackled to the living. His heart had failed him in the realization of his ghastly plight. He had died of fright.

The weary weeks of the voyage passed almost like centuries. With the others the simplehearted, superstitious Negro believed that soon his body was to be torn asunder, its fat utilized as grease and its blood as paint for the renovation of the ship. With the others he had often felt the stinging lash of the master's whip until his shoulders were pitifully striped. The whole voyage was for him one continued horror, interrupted only when tortured consciousness gave way and merciful sleep closed his eyelids.

Then, one midnight — a strange immobility of the lurching vessel! No longer the rushing waters thundered about her keel, but only a soft swishing sound was heard, no louder than the whirring of the seabird's wings.

Suddenly, an unwonted activity on the decks. . . . Next, the hold was opened, and an angel appeared as if out of the blue heavens, or up from the sea of the New World.

An angel! . . . A young man, very dark of hair and bright of countenance, with grace of body and movement, enveloped in a heavenly calm. In his hand he carried a huge basket filled with . . . could it be gifts for these unhappy ones?

Lightly he lowered himself into the ill-smelling place and there knelt in the midst of the unfortunate Negroes, a childlike smile on his countenance. Gently he soothed their fears, comforted their tormented bodies, bathed their wounds, and anointed them with cooling unctions. He slaked their thirst with the luscious juices of the orange and the mango, using his slender hands as cup.

So came a breath from very paradise to the abandoned and unhappy blacks. Confidence was restored to their anxious minds. Limbs, numb and lifeless, again felt the fresh blood coursing through them. Blood-glazed eyes lost their hunted look and came to resemble the eyes of men once more.

Such was the story hundreds of those might have told who now lay in the wretched old slave warehouse. Attentively, almost rapturously, they listened to every word of their Father in Christ, watching eagerly every change in the expression of his face, while, even as he spoke, the glimmer of lilac slanted in through the one small window. It now rested on a painting of the Last Judgment which the priest had set up in the miserable place.

Jesus Christ, the saintly young Jesuit was telling them, had also fallen into the hands of cruel and avaricious men. One had sold Him for thirty pieces of silver, far less than the price of a slave in the mart of Cartagena. . . . A robust Negro there might bring as much as three hundred dollars, whereas Christ was bartered away for only thirty pieces of silver.

"Look!" he said to the Negroes, as he held his crucifix high above them, that all might behold it. "See how much your good Jesus has suffered for you! See the streams of His Blood, coming from His wounds! Look on His pure Body, hanging from a Cross, a punishment inflicted on the greatest criminals only. To so much suffering your innocent Saviour willingly submitted. He drank the bitter cup of pain to the last drop. And why? Because He wished to give us an example of the way we should suffer; because He wished to banish evil from the world and blot out our sins.

"Will you, then, complain of your sorrows? Can you not suffer patiently some little pains as penance for your sins? Unite your sufferings to the Passion of Jesus and ask Him to pardon your faults!"

Then Ana Sabocana's beautiful young Pedro blessed his children in Christ, and so, taking up his cloak and the empty basket, he departed, leaving them consoled and strengthened with the thought of his presence and words.

The painting of the Last Judgment was left behind. It was to serve as a reminder of the necessity of contrition and penance for sin. Crudely executed though it was, it fulfilled its purpose in teaching the impressionable blacks the truths Father Pedro wished to bring home to them.

But one person there was who did not find inspiration

in it. This was Doña Carmen de Badajos, member of an illustrious family in Cartagena, a vain young woman, frivolous and irreligious. She had seen it exposed in the plaza before the Government Palace at a time when Father Claver was instructing the negro boys he had led there in procession from the church. She saw the painting and she laughed.

Chapter III

THE SHARP clanging of the bell above the iron-grilled doors of the College of San Ignacio brought the brother porter running quickly to answer.

A gentleman stood without — that is, Brother Emmanuel Lopez deemed him such, judged by his elegant attire and the air of distinction with which he bore himself. He wore a green velvet jacket and trousers, trimmed with many metal buttons, and leather boots, turned down. His finely pleated, lace-frilled shirt showed between the edges of an embroidered vest, over which hung a heavy gold chain and numerous amulets. On his arm he carried a long cloak with very wide collar and lapels and a green velour hat.

However, the manners of the "gentleman" left much to be desired, as the brother soon had reason to know.

"I wish to see Father Claver!" he announced in a voice so angry that he could scarcely articulate.

Brother Lopez trembled, for he was a meek man and the subject of his morning meditation, "Jesus Silent," was still with him. He admitted the stranger and showed him into the parlor, which boasted only a rude table, a few stiff-backed, cane-seated chairs and, high up on the walls, several faded prints of early members of the Society of Jesus.

The caller elevated a pair of luxuriant eyebrows in evident disdain of his surroundings. Ungraciously, he accepted the brother's invitation to make himself comfortable — a thing plainly impossible since his irate mood was in nowise tempered by the excessive heat of the day.

Having fulfilled this small but unpleasant mission, Brother Lopez departed with less decorum than his holy rule prescribed. He did not go in search of Father Claver, for he knew the Apostle had left the College shortly before to visit the Hospital of San Lazaro. Instead, he went directly to the office of the rector, Father Morello, and informed him that a caller waited.

The Rector was busily writing, composing an important document to be sent to the Superior General of the Society, Father General Vitteleschi, at Rome. But he instantly laid down his pen and like the most obedient novice went to answer the summons.

In the parlor he found the visitor, whose ire had mounted every instant since the brother had left him alone with his thoughts.

"Where is Father Claver? I asked for Father Claver, not for you!" the man said, impudently.

The rector appeared not to notice the extreme discourtesy. But he remarked in even tones and with a placid countenance that he regretted Father Claver was not to be interviewed at that time. The young priest had gone to visit the sick and to give religious instructions.

"You would hardly ever find him here at this hour," the Jesuit added. "When he is not instructing the slaves or visiting one of the hospitals he is usually hearing confessions in the church. If there is any message . . ."

Plainly much chagrined, the Spanish gentleman struck one lace-cuffed wrist against the other. "You can take the message," he said, impatiently. "It is to tell this meddlesome priest, from me, that if he does not stop interfering with my slaves, I'll . . . I'll . . ."

As gently as possible, although his patience was sorely tried by the impertinence and irreverence of the man, the Jesuit Superior questioned him. He felt certain he knew the nature of the grievance.

His surmise proved correct. The caller, Emmanuel Rodriguez, a slave owner and a man unscrupulous in conduct, protested that Father Claver exercised such a powerful influence over his "merchandise" that the slaves were unwilling to work on Sundays, alleging that that day belonged to the Lord. Also, that their numerous prayers and religious exercises rendered them disobedient to his commands.

Moreover, when they were whipped — and whipped all slaves ought to be, according to Don Emmanuel — they were so "hardened" that the chastisement did no good. The slave owner forbore to add that his pride had been sorely wounded when he discovered that his Negroes no longer feared him and that he had seen their lips moving in prayer when, according to his way of thinking, they should have been cowering in the dust, begging for mercy. This behavior on the part of creatures whom their thoughtless master deemed of no greater worth than beasts of burden had goaded him to an almost irrepressible fury.

Like the good son of San Ignacio that he was, Father Morello maintained his composure in this trying circumstance. Diverting the mind of his visitor into more pleasant channels he casually remarked on the arrival of a treasure-ship from Spain and from that interesting subject passed on to speak of the coffee and sugar crops.

Gradually Don Rodriguez relaxed a little. With that Father Morello, in turn, deemed it expedient to introduce a new note into the conversation. He took his guest wholly by surprise when he said, in straightforward manner:

"You tell me, Don Rodriguez, that Father Claver has

hurt your cause with your slaves. On the word of a priest I can assure you such is not the fact. True, this young man has a strong influence over them, but it is a good and helpful influence. His teachings are certain to make them better workers, more loyal and obedient than they would otherwise be. After all, these blacks have souls, have they not — even as you and I? But neither you nor I are capable of sacrificing ourselves as Father Claver is doing. He comes of noble family, even as you, my dear Señor! He has voyaged to this distant land by his own desire and offered himself to labor exclusively for the slaves. Now, my dear Señor . . . ?"

Don Emmanuel unwillingly complied with the inferential request and declared his identity.

"Thank you. My dear Señor Rodriguez, I can say to you that God's call to this young man was very evident. Our Father de Villegas, his Provincial at Barcelona, feared to oppose the Divine Will by denying his request that he be allowed to cóme here. And our Father Mejia, who brought Claver and several other youths of distinguished family from Spain to New Granada, could not say enough in praise of his virtue and talents. Father Claver is not a man who would interfere with anyone, unless duty required it. In this case, Señor, he feels he is following the divine wishes. As you know, we are all bound to do that.

"To convince you that this young religious practices what he preaches to the blacks, I will say that I have never gone to his room without finding him engaged in his prayers or penances. I have sometimes opened the door softly and have come upon him kneeling, a crown of thorns on his head and a rope about his neck, wholly absorbed in the sorrows of his Crucified Saviour. Believe me, Señor, when I assure you he is doing a great work, not alone for the slaves, but for you and for me who have need of prayer and penance."

Don Emmanuel had softened as Father Morello spoke. At the end he remained silent for some moments. Then he said:

"Thank you, Father. I am glad you told me this. I distrusted and disliked Father Claver. I believed him a busybody who wished to distinguish himself in the eyes of others. I believe you and I apologize for my bad manners and for the disrespect I showed you and this holy house. Forgive me, please, and accept this small offering — it is for Father Claver's work."

Don Emmanuel laid a substantial gift on the table.

"Please do not mention the donor's name. You may be certain I shall not come here to complain of the Father again. But, I regret to say, there are many slave owners who feel as I did a few moments ago. They are jealous of the powerful influence he has over their property and vex and thwart him at every opportunity. I will do my best to convert them to my present way of thinking."

Father Morello's tired eyes lighted as he bade farewell to Don Emmanuel.

"Alabado sea Dios!" "Praise be to God!" he said.

While this conversation was going on in the Jesuit College, the subject of it was trudging toward the Hospital of San Lazaro, where the unfortunate lepers of Cartagena and the surrounding country were housed.

Before setting out the priest had donned a habit of rough material and armed himself with an old broom and a basket of supplies for the sick. Laden with these he had gone down the Calle de la Media Luna and past the house of Don Pedro and Doña Isabel d'Urbina. In these two he was soon to find the most devoted friends. A few moments later he came to the tiny Jesuit Chapel, San Roque, at the juncture of the Calle el Éspiritu Santo, the original Residencia of the Fathers in Cartagena. One short block ahead he could see the arch in the Baluarte (Bastion) de San Antonio. Coming to this he sprang lightly upon it and continued his journey on the farther side.

He did not look toward the shimmering waters to see whether any ship was in sight, far down the Bay, or lying in the land-locked harbor after a long perilous voyage from the homeland. No one would ever know whether this denial of a natural instinct cost the young religious dearly or whether he had so steeled himself to mortification that he no longer remembered the queenly beauty of the turquoise and silver sea.

Father Pedro's face and hands showed blotches here and there — mosquito bites. His brethren at San Ignacio often remarked that Claver had never been seen to brush one of the pests from him although they were distracting at times.

The ardent Apostle had stopped at a number of the fine residences along the Calle de la Media Luna to fill the basket he now bore to his cherished lepers. Nowhere had he consented to enter and rest awhile. But he had stood as always, outside the door, eyes lowered, a winning smile on his lips, and asked for alms for the love of Christ.

Nowhere was he refused. Oranges and mangoes, plums and quinces and grapes; balsams of copaiba and tolú, sarsaparilla and ipecacuanha — these, and a small supply of scented waters comprised the contents of the basket. Although he himself scarcely remembered the taste or smell of the delicious fruits and cordials, Father Pedro was content because they would bring comfort and joy to his black children. He remembered with gratitude the kind Spanish ladies who had provided this happiness for priest and lepers alike — Doña Isabel d'Urbina and others, whom he had never met but whose charities were well known to him.

At that very hour Brother Estaban Añaja, in charge of San Lazaro Hospital, was devoutly wishing that Father Claver would appear; he generally arrived about that hour. The brother was holding tightly to his nose with one hand as with the other he bore a medicinal preparation to the cot of a leper. The good religious had never been able to overcome his repugnance for his work; for that reason he had little success in lightening the physical distress or the spirits of his patients.

Father Claver also attended the sick at San Sebastiano, located not far from the cathedral and the residence of the Bishop, Fray Francisco de Sotomayer. But it appeared that he entertained a decided preference for San Lazaro. Even Brother Estaban, who confessed that he was not yet ready to suffer martyrdom, knew the reason. Among the lepers there was abundant opportunity for sacrifice. Not only did the deadly odor of decaying flesh assail a man's nostrils at every instant, but the appearance of the victims was often so repulsive as to cause those who ventured near them to faint. Naturally, such persons never again paid a call on the premises, however strong their sympathies might be.

For instance — the leper toward whom Brother Estaban was at that moment shuffling, presented the aspect of a living skeleton. His head was eaten nearly to the bone by the ravages of the fell disease. Here and there patches of whitened skin showed; in places it was falling away from the victim.

In other cases, only half the face was diseased; by contrast with the healthy flesh its rottenness was the more repellent. Beneath the bed covering, composed in awful dignity, were the wrecks of once noble specimens of manhood or womanhood. Sometimes legs had completely fallen apart as the germ gradually unfastened the joints sustaining the living members; sometimes hands had dropped

away. Yet these terrible evidences of the foul plague were
bearable in comparison with the putridness of the raw
flesh of certain lepers who were being slowly consumed in
a mass of noxious sores.

These were but a few of the forms leprosy might assume,
so that Moses had well characterized it when he called it
tsarath, meaning, "terrible disease."

Before Father Claver had begun his visits to this charnel
house outside the city walls, a priest had occasionally come
there to offer up the Holy Sacrifice. But always he had
found it necessary to depart as soon as possible. If the
Apostle of the Slaves experienced a like revulsion; if at
times he was tempted to rush for the door and escape into
the fresh air, he gave no indication of it. The religious of
San Juan de Dios, in charge of the institution, sometimes
remarked to one another that, even though the Jesuit was
a holy man, his heroic ministrations would be impossible
without a special providence of God.

It was certain that Claver loved his work, for on every
occasion when his Community held festive recreation he
would hurry to his beloved San Lazaro to be received with
an almost adoring welcome by the lepers.

On this particular day the Spanish captain, Pedro Doriola, was strolling below the Baluarte de San Antonio when
he espied the priest hurrying along in the full rays of the
sun, although the mata-raton bushes afforded a grateful
shade on the opposite side of the path. The captain had
never met Claver but he had heard of him.

He hastened after him and saluted respectfully.

"You are so cheerful, Father," he said, "that I am
tempted to ask where you are going."

The smiling eyes of Pedro Claver looked full into the
eyes of his questioner, as the Apostle replied, gaily:

"I am going to keep carnival with my poor at San

Lazaro." And, before Captain Doriola had time to reply, the swift-footed figure had passed beyond. Claver's head was lowered and Doriola rightly concluded that he was praying and would prefer to be alone.

The captain was not a little curious about the affair. As others in similar circumstance had done he followed the hurrying figure, at a little distance.

At the door of the church attached to San Lazaro all the lepers who were able to leave their beds were waiting. Those unable to stand were supported in the arms of their companions. Their faces shone with joy as they saw their "Good Father" coming toward them.

Father Pedro knelt in their midst and recited a few short prayers. He next distributed his gifts, reserving a portion for those inside the hospital. Then he gave an earnest exhortation, encouraging the lepers to bear their sorrows in union with their suffering Lord and for His love.

When he had finished, the Apostle sat down on a large stone and heard the confessions of those who approached by themselves or were carried to him.

Captain Doriola was amazed at the sight. For this little priest showed no fear of infection at the proximity of creatures so hideously tainted. Yet in his novitiate days in Tarragona, whence the captain himself had come, Pedro Claver had looked often on the souvenirs of earthly grandeur and power. With his novice companions he had walked about the rugged hill with its steep alleys and houses built of solid Roman masonry. He must often have stopped to examine the fragment, immured in the wall of an ancient palace, which bore the epitaph of a Roman charioteer — "Auriga." Below, the whole Tarragonian province was green with olive and almond groves and fields of flax waved in the breezes sweeping from those majestic heights.

There was nothing in common between the two pictures — Claver in his former illustrious setting and Claver paying a visit to a pesthouse where he was obliged to hear confessions in the street because of the ruined condition of the chapel. Although he was a good Christian, Captain Doriola could not understand such a sacrifice.

The lithe figure of the priest had now disappeared within the hospital. Forgetting that he greatly feared contact with the lepers, the captain went up to the little group, seated on the ground and enjoying the feast their Good Father had provided for them. He asked why Claver had gone into the hospital and what he was accustomed to do there.

Ah! That question was easily answered. He had gone to tend those in the extremity of the loathsome malady. Some, who could not use their arms or who had no arms to use, were being fed by their Father in God who, to encourage them, would himself partake of a little of their food and eat from the same dish with them.

Captain Doriola whistled low under his fine mustachios. He had known many good and holy priests, but he had not hitherto met one such as this.

The lepers continued their recital without the need of coaxing.

Sometimes Father Claver held what he termed "banquets" for his sick. For the principal feasts of Jesus and Mary he engaged charitably inclined persons to provide some extra gifts, that he might "feast" his children. He also begged that a band of musicians be sent to the hospital to dispense lively airs for their entertainment.

The Spanish officer remained about the premises a little longer. He hoped Father Claver might reappear. He did not.

The captain had no desire to go inside the leper hospital. The sight of virulent sores and the odor of rotting flesh were not to his liking. He could admire but not imitate the Apostle.

Flicking an imaginary speck from his velvet puffs, he tossed some coins to the poor lepers outside the gate and continued on his way.

Chapter IV

DOÑA ISABEL D'URBINA was paying an unwonted visit
to the quarters of the women slaves belonging to her
household. She was somewhat curious about certain papers
her young attendant, Liseta, had received from Father
Pedro Claver. A little humbly and with some embarrass-
ment, the wife of Don Pedro d'Urbina had requested the
girl to show these papers to her. It was the first time she
had asked a favor of one of the blacks.

Gathering her ample skirts about her stately figure, Doña
Isabel stooped, on reaching the door of the hut, for she
was very tall, and entered the wide, low-ceilinged room
where the cots of the Negresses were arranged in rows.
She knew that Liseta would be alone at that hour; the
others had duties to perform in the mansion and would
not return until evening.

The young slave was sitting on her cot with her treasures spread out for her mistress' inspection. They were
little slips of paper made precious by the handwriting of
Father Claver. She was regarding them with an expression
of pride. Slaves did not generally own anything of value.
These writings, in the native dialect of the little negro
slave, were of great value, and now the fine lady of the
house had come to examine them, perhaps even to envy
the girl and wish they were her own!

Isabel could not know what went on in Liseta's active brain. Had she known she might have been gravely displeased. For just then Liseta was dwelling with complacency on the thought that, in the heavenly country of which Father Claver often spoke, a slave might "sit beside" a fine lady who had once owned her body, but never her soul. And that she, Liseta, might be wearing a crown as bright as that which would adorn the white brow of Doña Isabel. The girl had not yet acquired the virtue of humility; she had learned avidly but she was still a neophyte in the class of Negresses who met semi-weekly in an acacia grove to listen to Father Claver's instructions.

Liseta explained the writings on the various papers, for Doña Isabel was unfamiliar with the negro dialects.

The young priest had told his children what God wanted of them, what He insisted on having. Every human being must obey His will at all times, not merely when it was convenient to do so. Above all, one must never do anything displeasing to God. And the more a soul was freed from pride the more would she be able to love God and understand His beautiful lessons.

Liseta omitted to read certain counsels of the Apostle on the virtues of obedience and submission to authority. Father Claver had said: "Obey those over you and submit to them for the sake of our Lord. Do all you can to please them and never lose your peace of mind. . . ." Doña Isabel would be certain to concur in that!

Unfortunately, there were things the slave girl much preferred to obedience — that point was hard to accept — but the priest had insisted upon it. As for remaining silent in time of correction, another admonition, that was not difficult to one in Liseta's position. For to talk back to Doña Isabel or to her sister, the Señorita Jeromina, would be to incur severe chastisement. Isabel's virtue was of a high order, but she was a spirited young woman and insisted upon the complete subjugation of her slaves to her will. Happily, she was not a harsh or unreasonable mistress.

In response to the lady's eager questioning about what went on in the slave warehouse and the acacia grove during Father Claver's visits, the girl described the touching scenes and incidents.

It seemed that the Apostle possessed marvelous patience. Many of the older Negroes, who had suffered most at the hands of cruel masters, found it hard to bend their necks to the yoke of Christian teaching. With these it was necessary to exercise the greatest tact, fortitude, and generosity. When Liseta described the sores that covered the bodies of a large number of these blacks, Doña Isabel shuddered and held up a jeweled hand to bid her omit such nauseating details.

Once Liseta had followed close on the footsteps of the holy man as he was returning from the bedsides of the sick. A brother coadjutor accompanied him. The Negress had listened carefully to the conversation that reached her ears at that slight distance.

The brother was a young religious who had accompanied the father to the slave pens to see for himself what all Cartagena admired and reverenced. But he advanced no farther than the door. The unpleasant odors drifting out and the glimpse of so many wretchedly emaciated and disfigured blacks proved too much for his endurance. He had withdrawn, humbled and shamed by the realization of his lack of courage in the face of the sublime magnanimity of Father Claver. He had waited outside the place until the priest accomplished his mission, which was to hear the confession of a dying Negro and give him the holy Viaticum.

Liseta had heard the young brother expostulating with the heroic Apostle as the two religious walked back to the college. On that occasion, out of consideration for his companion, Claver chose to walk on the shady side of the street.

To the protests of the brother over his disregard of his health, Father Claver had replied in words which now Liseta repeated in her own way to Doña Isabel.

"What am I doing? Ah, brother! Are the little sufferings I must undergo in the performance of my mission to be compared with a single pang suffered by the Divine Master? If He had no thought for His Immaculate Flesh, should I treat my miserable body delicately?

"If Christ did not complain when the crown of thorns was placed on His brow, why should I be unable to endure the odor of the slave pens? He was silent when He was nailed to the cross and should I complain of the insignificant pains my labors cause me?

"My Jesus died for me, and ought I not be anxious to satisfy His thirst for souls and to spend the short days of my life serving Him in the persons of His unfortunate children? He has said that we do good to Him when we do good to our fellow beings. May God grant me sufficient strength to sacrifice myself in fulfilling the sacred duty of charity He has imposed on me! May I be ready to shed my blood to save the souls confided to my care!"

As if the words were addressed to her personally, Doña Isabel d'Urbina felt them seeping into her heart as the sunny waters of the Caribbean stole up on the sea wall of the old city.

Liseta did not yet understand why Father Claver was satisfied to mingle freely with those whom she considered the refuse of humankind; why he wore a habit patched in a dozen places and alpargates — crudely fashioned hempen sandals — so worn that they were almost falling off his feet. This extraordinary young Catalan noble outstripped in abnegation the lowliest lay brother in Cartagena of the Indies — and there were many of the latter, for the Queen of the Caribes was a veritable spiritual fortress of monasteries.

Liseta had actually been the recipient of Father Claver's special bounty. Hearing that a slave trader was approaching the bay, she had sent a negro boy running to the Jesuit college to find the priest and inform him of the fact. The reward for her act of charity was a Mass offered for her intentions by the Apostle himself. Her regard for the "Good Father" of the slaves had somewhat increased when this was explained to her.

Doña Isabel listened attentively to the account of a marvelous apostolate of spiritual and corporal mercy connected with this particular incident.

Upon learning of the arrival of the slave trader, the Apostle had immediately called two stalwart Negroes. In the hands of one he placed one end of a long pole; he himself took up the other end. Two baskets containing fruits, medicines, and bandages were attached to the pole. The second Negro was to relieve the first when the latter grew weary of his burden. No one was appointed to relieve Father Pedro.

Her eyes bulging from their sockets, Liseta had followed the trio down the Calle de Media Luna to the sea wall. From that vantage she could look down on the slave ship. She saw the Apostle descending into the hold, where a mass of writhing, manacled humanity lay huddled together. Only when the keen eyes of the Negress discerned two dead men among the unfortunates did she flee in horror.

She had seen sufficient to satisfy her curiosity. Father Claver had passed across the cargo of living, mutilated, and suffering human flesh, leaving no one untended. He had assured the miserable creatures that no great evil was in store for them; that their limbs were not destined to be hacked asunder and the fat utilized as grease or their blood sucked out to serve as paint for the clumsy slave ship. Nor were their bones to be ground into fine powder to provide fertilizer for the soil of New Granada. Contrary to all this, everything would be well with them because One was watching tenderly over them; and that One was God, a kind and loving Father. In His great pity and mercy He had sent a lowly servant of His, most unworthy but devoted to them, to dispense His bounties, to allay the fears of His children and to prepare them for a great reward to come.

Father Pedro had knelt on the floor amidst the tortured bleeding bodies and taken them to his heart, rocking them as a mother might do.

Liseta faithfully relayed these items to Doña Isabel, so that it was fully an hour before that lady prepared to take her departure. More and more was her generous heart stirred to its depths as she learned of the character and work of one who was universally and rightly deemed a great servant of God.

When Isabel returned to the house she found her sister Jeromina eagerly awaiting her. There was wonderful news from "home." A letter had arrived from Sevilla. The younger sister had held it, unsealed, until Isabel should be present so that together they might revel in its contents.

Two dark glossy heads bent excitedly over the bit of delicate parchment on which the loved ones in the homeland had set down the important news that had occurred since they had last dispatched a letter from those friendly shores.

All the Sevillanos had attended the Romeria, the great religious picnic in Sevilla, with its procession of gaily decorated oxcarts, the oxen adorned with ribbon streamers of every hue. Isabel and Jeromina had often participated, sitting in the first cart which bore a large banner encircled by a cluster of tall wax candles. Past the Giralda Tower; the bull ring, which never failed to provide an animated scene on Sunday afternoons; through the Plaza San Fernando, the largest square in the city, the colorful procession had wound, the merry songs of the young people ringing loud and clear. Many of the ladies were costumed as characters in the paintings of the old Spanish masters.

The Sevillanos knew how to get the most and best out of life, and they took full advantage of that knowledge.

Jeromina, who was of a lively temperament, talked volubly and excitedly as she recalled memories dearly cherished. Isabel sat silent while the younger girl described in glowing terms the pastimes they had enjoyed together before Isabel had sailed to New Granada to become a bride, and before Jeromina had quickly followed, to keep her dear one company in the New World.

The wife of Don Pedro d'Urbina was not thinking of these things, however. Her shell-pink ears were tinted a deeper color as she bent over the finely traced characters in the letter. In place of them it suddenly seemed to her as if a bright painting was stretched on an easel before her. On it she saw the figure of a young priest whose forehead was already lined by the cares and burdens of a self-imposed martyrdom, whose shoulders were already stooped as a result of ceaseless drudgery for the slaves.

He was bending low in the filthy hold of a slave ship, just arrived from the coasts of Africa. He was laying one pure cheek against the cheek of a manacled Negro, the latter tainted with foul disease brought on by lack of decent food, fresh air, and a celestial hope. With slender fingers the young priest-nobleman was touching the sores of the helpless creatures and binding the wounds inflicted by the slave owner's lash.

Isabel d'Urbina knew she must do something more than she had already done to promote the apostolate of Father Pedro Claver. She must deny herself and so provide more pesos for the needy and sorrowful blacks. She must refrain from sending to Sevilla for expensive laces and silks, jeweled combs, and other costly luxuries dear to the heart of every highborn Spanish lady.

Isabel could not know that in the distant future, when her graceful head had bowed before the trials and sorrows of life, she was to offer her most precious gift to Father Pedro Claver. Long after her adored husband, her father, and others who cherished her would be gone from the city by the chanting waters of the Caribbean, this privilege would be hers.

The gift of a certain cedar-wood box, encrusted with precious metals . . . her final offering to the Jesuit Apostle who was to care for her soul during the long years.

Chapter V

AT THE HOUR of Ave Maria the trade wind blew from the sea. The sailors lying in at the port of Cartagena strolled about on the sands or squatted on the decks of their ships and talked of the things men remember when they are far from home and loved ones. They talked of shepherds leading their flocks along the banks of the Guadalquivir River at Cordova; of the curio shops in Toledo where they hoped to sell the unique objects gathered in every port touched during the voyage; of the warm Biscayan air wafted over the jade-colored Bay of San Sebastiano — of these and other familiar things left behind, for how long no sailorman could tell.

The bay was rippled as the outer surface of a vast shell, a delicate mauve close to the shore, farther off the crimson of the bouganvillea, the large, full-petaled, almost purple blossoms crowding thickly on their bushes. In the walled gardens of the old city, the hibiscus flowers were closing their petals at the end of the day and the yellow blossoms of the icaco sent out a subtle perfume.

At the doors in the Calle de Cuartel, Street of the Barracks, soldiers exchanged tales of lusty adventure and the little burros in the Calle de las Carretas, Street of the Carts, lifted their long ears and looked about. Shutters swung open and faces peered from latticed windows and balconies, the latter hung with straw matting to ensure privacy.

Men and women walked in the streets, "tomando el fresco" — taking the air — and very gratefully after the lengthened brilliance of the day. They walked slowly past the solidly built houses, houses long and low for the most part, frequently surrounded by lengths of wall that gave them a monastic air. In the loggias, which every patio boasted, the Spanish families, the "flor y nata" — flower and cream of society — sat and drank a coconut or two.

In the patio of the fine stone house on the Calle de la Media Luna, the home of Don Pedro and Doña Isabel d'Urbina, two Spanish gentlemen were relaxing in comfortable arm chairs. One was Don Juan d'Estrada, father of Doña Isabella, the other her vigorous, tall, and handsome husband, Don Pedro d'Urbina. Don Juan, who cherished for the great conquistadors all the admiration of a highborn Spanish gentleman, was speaking of events that had preceded the beginning of the slave trade in New Granada and Father Pedro Claver's apostolate.

Long before the coming of the slave traders and their human cargo to those shores the Indians had roamed, unmolested, over the land. They too had suffered wrongs at the hands of the white man. It was of these wrongs that Don Juan was thinking.

Until the arrival of de Heredia and the founding of Cartagena, in 1533, few ships had entered the bay. Therefore, the history of the years up to that time was practically spiritless. But such a well-favored harbor could not long remain unknown, and so had come Heredia, who was to do great things for the little Indian town then called Calamar.

"The year of his discovery of our noble city," Don Juan said, "Heredia was made governor of the territory extending from the mouth of the River Magdalena to

Dairen. He had already achieved distinction in the New World where he had triumphed over many difficulties. In his youth he had shown himself courageous and ready for all hazards."

Don Juan gazed fixedly at the massive chandelier over his head while changing his posture — his bones were no longer supple — and continued.

"Unlike other Spanish captains sailing for these parts, Heredia brought no fine cloth stuffs or rich furniture with him. He loaded his trusty ship with ammunition, cannon, and muskets; with swords, lances, and defensive armor fitted for warfare in the tropics. He also brought with him a barge, so constructed that it could sail up rivers and penetrate small creeks, something a larger craft could not do.

"Heredia stopped at various islands to take on men. With these and fifty fine horses, most of which later perished in the stormy Caribbean, he continued his voyage. It is thought that his ships entered the harbor of Cartagena by way of Boca Grande.

"From the beginning, Heredia waged a continuous warfare against the Indians, sometimes defeated, sometimes victorious. Fortunately an old Indian named Coronche, whom he had taken prisoner, became very useful as guide — the Conquistador was very anxious to penetrate inland.

"It was probably the lack of water in the interior that caused him to retrace his steps to Cartagena and here found his city. This he did on January twenty-first, 1533, under the high patronage of San Sebastiano."

As if he were reading from a book the old man went on with his story:

"The Indians called the Spaniards 'Christians.' They believed them to be thieves and plunderers. For that reason the Indian chiefs prepared to resist them to the death.

"Through various treaties concluded with the savages, Heredia had become the possessor of much gold dust and rare gems. He wished to enrich the motherland as well as himself, but he was also keenly desirous of implanting the Faith in New Granada. He smashed all the idols the Indians had set up to worship. To appease the red men he distributed presents among them — hawk bells, red caps, and axes. He amassed enormous riches, but these he divided with Philip, his sovereign, and his men. According to the compromise entered into before Heredia left Spain for America he was to give one fifth of his treasure to the monarch.

"Heredia was a generous man. He made large contributions to the hospital founded at an early date in Cartagena; paid his captains liberally and had sufficient funds left to bestow six thousand ducats on each of his followers.

"The old Indian guide was the first to inform his master that beneath the many tumuli or mogotes — sand hills running out on the beach — treasure lay buried. Heredia endured incredible hardships in his frequent expeditions into the forests and across the mountains of the interior, robbing all the Indian graves of their gold. One of these graves, that of an Indian chief named Tolú, yielded ten thousands castellanos[1] in pure gold.

"It seemed that Heredia could never find sufficient tasks of peril and conquest to satisfy his intrepid spirit. When he was sixty years old he started on an important expedition. Unfortunately it was not successful. The gallant Conquistador eventually perished off the shores of Cadiz.

"He had set out from that city to seek his fortunes in the New World. So to Cadiz he was returning at the end of a long full life when a sudden tempest overturned his

---

[1] A castellano then equaled about eleven present-day American dollars.

ship as it had nearly made port. All his men perished in the turbulent sea. People standing on the beach, watching Heredia, the sole survivor, struggling in the treacherous billows, were overcome with grief when they saw his body dashed on the rocks, then swept far out to sea.

"When Heredia died," commented Don Juan, sadly, "the heroic age of Cartagena passed. He had ruled the city honorably for thirty years previous to his last voyage to Spain. He was active, brave, constant, and even in his declining years never lost the dauntlessness that marked his pioneer adventures into the wilderness of New Granada. We have not the honor of guarding his bones in our midst but we perpetuate his memory with reverence and affection. The people loved him; he was a peacemaker among the quarrelsome and of forgiving nature. He had never thought it wrong to rob the Indian graves — although we understand otherwise."

Doña Isabel had joined the two men during the latter part of her father's narration.

"I wonder, father, whether Pedro has ever heard the plea Bishop Las Casas made in behalf of the Indians of our Kingdom?" she asked.

Don Juan was not disinclined to speak of one for whom he entertained the highest admiration. Drawing forward a chair for Isabel, like the true grandee of Spain that he was, he began, in happy vein:

"Certain bishops and priests of Spain had visited New Granada during Heredia's regime and protested against the ill-treatment accorded the Indians. The Emperor, Charles V, was much disturbed by the reports of conditions as represented to him by these churchmen, especially the great Las Casas. At the Bishop's suggestion the celebrated Code of Laws known as the 'Laws of the Indies' was drawn up by the Great Council of the Realm. It confirmed the wise ordinances of the monarch's grandmother, Isabel the

Catholic. This Code instructed the Spaniards to treat the Indians well, not to make slaves of them; to improve their living conditions and to teach them the truths of the Catholic Faith."

"And the 'wise ordinances' were not carried out over here!" Don Pedro d'Urbina remarked.

"Far from it," Don Juan said. "Far from it. The Spaniards in this kingdom laughed at the laws, then put them aside. If in certain quarters they seemed disposed to obey them they gave only a mock obedience."

"Father," Doña Isabel interposed, "you have a manuscript copy of Bishop Las Casas' speech to His Majesty, have you not?"

"Yes, Isabel," Don Juan replied. "It is in the top drawer of my secretary. You may bring it to me, if you will."

Ever thoughtful for his wife's comfort, Don Pedro volunteered to go for the manuscript. In a few minutes he returned and placed it in his father-in-law's hands.

The old man laid aside his pipe and opened the pages, almost reverently. Clearing his throat, he began to read in a trembling voice:

"I was one of the first who went to America; neither curiosity nor interest prompted me to undertake so long and dangerous a voyage; the saving of the souls of the heathen was my main object.

"Why was I not permitted, even at the expense of my blood, to ransom so many thousand souls who fell unhappy victims to avarice or lust? I have been an eyewitness to such cruel treatment of the Indians as is too horrid to be mentioned at this time. It is said that barbarous executions were necessary to punish or check the rebellion of the Americans, but to whom was this owing? Did not these people receive the Spaniards who first came among them with gentleness and humanity? Did they not show more joy, in proportion, in lavishing treasures upon them, than the Spaniards did in receiving them?

"But our avarice was not satisfied. Though they gave up to us their lands and their riches, we would tear them from their wives, their children, their liberties. To blacken these unhappy people, their enemies assert that they are scarce human creatures — but it is we who ought to blush for having been less men and more barbarous than they.

"What right have we to enslave a people that are born free and whom we disturbed, though they never offended us? They are represented as a stupid people, addicted to vice — but have they not contracted most of their vices from the example of the Christians? And, as to those vices peculiar to themselves, have not the Christians quickly exceeded therein? Nevertheless, it must be granted that the Indians still remain untainted by many vices usual among Europeans, such as ambition, blasphemy, treachery, and many like monsters which have not yet taken place with them; they have scarcely an idea of them, so that, in effect, all the advantage we can claim is to have more elevated notions of things and our natural faculties more unfolded and more cultivated than theirs.

"Do not let us flatter our corruptions or voluntarily blind ourselves; all nations are equally free; one nation has no right to infringe upon the freedom of any other; let us do toward these people as we would that they should have done toward us if they had landed on our shores with the same superiority of strength. And, indeed, why should not things be equal on both sides? How long has the might of the strongest been allowed to be the balance of justice?"

Don Juan's voice appeared tired. Laying a soft hand on her father's arm, Isabel said affectionately:

"You are fatigued, father. If you please, I will read."

The old man unwillingly relinquished his beloved manuscript and his daughter read on in a strong clear voice that must greatly have pleased the good Bishop could he have heard it.

"What part of the Gospel gives sanction to such a doctrine? In what part of the whole earth did the Apostles and the first promulgators of the Gospel ever claim a right over the lives, the freedom or the substance of the Gentiles?

"What a strange method is this of propagation of the Gospel, that holy law of grace, which, from being slaves of sin, initiates us into the freedom of the children of God? Will it be possible for us to inspire them with a love for its dictates, while they are so exasperated at being dispossessed of that invaluable blessing, liberty? The Apostles themselves submitted to chains but loaded no man with them. Christ came to free, not to enslave us. Submission to the Faith He left ought to be a voluntary act and should be brought about by persuasion, gentleness and reason."

The Bishop further declared that many thousands had perished "through want, fatigue, merciless punishment, cruelty, and barbarity. If the blood of one man, unjustly shed, calls loudly for vengeance, how strong must be that of the many unhappy creatures which is being shed daily?"

Isabel d'Urbina laid down the manuscript in the midst of a solemn silence.

After a moment Don Juan said, a little bitterly:

"The King applauded the Bishop's speech and gave his word that he would second it. But, unfortunately, as happens today, so many influential persons were interested in perpetuating the system of oppression and cruelty that nothing was done to remedy the condition of the poor Indians."

Don Pedro d'Urbina bit his lip and toyed in annoyed fashion with his wife's silk sleeve. When he spoke he nipped off his words so brusquely that Isabel glanced toward him in surprise.

"A man cannot always do as he wishes in matters of this

kind," he said. "He cannot, for instance, be present on every part of his plantation at the same time, and the office of overseer is not calculated to attract meek men."

His wife did not hear the conversation that followed. Her thoughts had drifted into another channel.

She was thinking of the young noble, Father Pedro Claver, who was following the ideals of Bishop Las Casas as no man in New Granada had ever followed them — including the venerated Father Alfonso de Sandoval himself.

Doña Isabel knew that Father Claver tended not only the souls but the bodies of the unhappy slaves; that he cleansed their sores, ate with them, and even swept out their squalid huts. And at night, when all Cartagena slept save the cloistered ones who were keeping vigil, this young priest, although sorely tired after the hard day's labors, this sweet servant of Christ, rose to gird himself with instruments of penance and, in the gallery of the old college, to follow the Way of the Cross.

Isabel d'Urbina had another thought. It seemed a heaven-sent inspiration.

She must seek this man of God, this martyr of holy love, and beg him to undertake the care of her soul.

Chapter VI

DOÑA ISABEL D'URBINA had taken a great resolution and was following it out. She had come to the dingy little chapel of the Jesuit Fathers in the Calle de San Ignacio, opening wide her lustrous eyes as she entered that she might better see within after the brilliance of the streets.

At the door she had been chagrined to meet Antonia, a slave woman belonging to a neighbor. Antonia would be certain to relay to her family the news that Isabel had visited the chapel at an hour when Father Claver was hearing the confessions of the slaves. However, nothing could be done about it. And, certainly, it was not a shameful act.

The priest's confessional was located at the rear, in the hottest part of the sacred place. Several rows of female Negroes were grouped about it. On the opposite side of the chapel a few male slaves were engaged in their devotions.

Isabel knelt in an inconspicuous place, on a cushion she had brought with her for the purpose. Her position was an entirely new one to the highborn lady. Many of the blacks suffered from noxious diseases contracted through unhealthful living quarters, lack of proper nourishment, and drudgery in the silver mines or on the tobacco and sugar plantations. The odors emanating from their worn bodies were decidedly unpleasant, even at that distance.

Doña d'Urbina found somewhat amusing the little table before Claver's confessional. It was piled with fruits, lotions, and trinkets given the Apostle by the Spanish ladies of Cartagena. These gifts were distributed to his spiritual children who had shown the most improvement in virtue and in the knowledge of Christian doctrine during the week.

Almost an hour passed. Isabel had become very weary from the discomfort and nervous tension she was forced to endure. It seemed that the Apostle would be in his confessional until late in the evening, for the number of black penitents was constantly increasing. Jeromina would be expecting her sister to return in time to give orders for the evening meal. It was possible Isabel might not gain access to Father Claver. Unless . . .

She rose stiffly from her knees, shook out the folds of her silk gown to adjust its graceful lines and proceeded directly across the chapel.

An elderly Negress was emerging from the confessional as she did so. She need not hurry, however, for the slaves, watching her movements, fell back, awed and astonished by the sight of so beautiful a creature under such extraordinary circumstances. Fine ladies were accustomed to patronize the other fathers in the college. Or they went to the cathedral or to Santo Domingo for their confessions.

A little frightened by her temerity, Isabel entered the confessional and knelt down. But she was unable to utter a word.

After a moment Father Claver addressed her. Gently, yet firmly, he told her it would have been better had she not come there. That he was dedicated to the service of the slaves; that there were other confessors who could help

her much better than he could. However, if she wished
now to make her confession to him, he would hear it.

The holy presence and the kindliness of the young priest,
despite his admonition, comforted and reassured Isabel.
Taking courage in the thought that for a few blessed
moments she was in the hands of a saint she made her
confession honestly, then waited for the counsel she hoped
he might give.

She was not disappointed. The Jesuit Apostle spoke to
the highborn lady very graciously, very humbly, in a
manner that revealed him to be an enlightened director
of souls. When he had finished, he unburdened his priestly
heart of a great load of the love of God which filled it to
overflowing and must be shared with someone. Although
his penitent was a woman of wealth and position, Father
Claver recognized that here was a noble soul, needing his
help.

Isabel's heart beat rapidly as she heard the quiet voice
repeating, slowly and distinctly, several maxims which as
her confessor he urged her to practice in her daily life.
As she bent her lovely head lest she lose a word, the
Apostle of the Slaves said:

"I shall look for God everywhere.

"I shall do everything for the greater glory of God.

"I shall seek nothing in this world save to sanctify my
own soul and the souls of others."

Father Pedro then opened his heart to relieve it of
another burden that pressed on him. He confided to
Isabel his great desire to enlist the sympathies and the aid
of others in his work for the slaves. His unhappy spiritual
children were the victims of a grievous wrong which the
Church deplored and against which her anointed ministers
were waging a ceaseless warfare. Anything, he said, that
his penitent could do to help these needy ones and to
interest others in their well-being would be done for

Jesus Himself, and Jesus Himself would reward the act abundantly.

When Father Claver ceased speaking, Isabel faintly asked whether she might hope to have him permanently as her confessor and spiritual guide.

At that he turned slightly toward her, yet keeping his head inclined and his eyes modestly veiled. He replied in a straightforward way that her request could be granted on one condition. She must wait until all the slaves had been confessed before approaching him in the sacred tribunal. For, he said, he had given his life to these forgotten and abused human creatures and he would keep to that determination, with the divine help, to the end of his life.

Her heart singing for thankfulness, Isabel agreed to the condition and left the confessional.

They had told her that Claver often placed his cloak over ulcerous Negroes; that he utilized it as a bed for the sick in the hospitals of San Sebastiano and San Lazaro. It would seem that the cloak must be in a very unsanitary condition. . . . Isabel wondered a little about that. For she had noticed that a delicate perfume seemed to proceed from it as her confessor leaned toward her, one slender hand hiding a forehead already deeply lined for one so young. Claver allowed himself so little sleep that it could not be otherwise. This, with his penances and heroic labors and the secret anguish that wore on him as he witnessed so much misery among the blacks had taken their toll of his brave and generous youth.

The priest had given his penitent a paper on which a few counsels were written in delicate hand. This paper Isabel drew from her bodice, in the depths of her sedan chair, where no prying eyes might witness her action. . . .

"One who wishes to progress in virtue should know herself; knowing herself, she despises herself; ignoring herself, she becomes proud and arrogant."

The wife of Don Pedro d'Urbina hung her head. The hot blood dyed her cheeks — Father de Sandoval, Claver's predecessor, had not been accustomed to speak so strongly to her. It seemed that she had been a spoiled child all her life. . . .

"In all persons she should see God and honor His image in them.

"She should meditate often on the uncertainty of life and the certainty of death and should encourage herself to labor and suffer, remembering that soon there will no longer be time to meditate or to merit."

At home, and seated in her favorite armchair, whose wrought-leather back showed the arms of Spain and the hat of its sovereign, Doña Isabel fingered absent-mindedly the labellum of a gorgeous vanilla orchid growing beside the open door. Her brow was contracted in sober thought. Soon she clapped her hands as summons to Liseta.

The girl appeared at once and stood submissively before her mistress. She wondered whether Doña Isabel had learned of her defection of a few nights previous — the young Negress had stolen from her bed and gone to a dance held in an acacia grove bordering the sea. What if one of the slaves on a neighboring estate had been found out in the wrongdoing and had told on Liseta?

The young slave trembled. Doña Isabel's delicate wrists could direct stinging blows with the whip, not brutal, yet to be remembered, were her orders disregarded.

To the girl's surprise her mistress had nothing to say about the affair of the cumbia. Only to Father Claver need that be made known and at the proper time and place. He would undoubtedly administer strong medicine in the form of an admonition and a stout penance to the sinner. But he would not whip Liseta.

Isabel was speaking.

"Liseta," she began, slowly, "I have tried to be a good mistress to you — "

Plainly, the lady was in a strange mood. Yet she would assuredly not look that way if she were about to inflict punishment on her slave.

For once the girl was bereft of the power of speech. She could only roll her tongue over her lips and bob her head vigorously so that every ringlet of her hair and her large crescent-shaped earrings danced up and down.

Her mistress continued.

"I want to say that — I am sorry I ever punished you when — when I was overwrought and lost my temper. Mind — I do not say that I regret having punished you when you deserved it. But I am saying that — in future I shall always try to give you a good example. Now, go, and see that you give me no trouble in the future. In general you are a good girl. Try to improve from day to day and soon there will be no necessity for chastising you."

In her astonishment Liseta continued to roll her tongue and blink unsteadily. When she left Isabel's presence she proceeded directly to the stables where she knew Manuel, Don Pedro's groom, would be engaged in his duties. To this faithful ally she expressed the opinion that her mistress was not feeling well. For, not ten minutes before, for some unaccountable reason, she had begged Liseta's pardon!

The young slave had left the room but a moment when Don Pedro d'Urbina approached his wife's side. He had returned from a visit to the sugar plantation a few hours before to find her missing. He was a little weary; tired lines showed beneath the fine eyes that somewhat shadowed his face as did his abundant blue-black hair. On the round cedar table near by rested Isabel's mantilla, with the cushion she had taken to the chapel. Don Pedro glanced at the latter in evident surprise.

"You were gone a long time, my dear," he said. "May

I inquire what was the important mission that occupied my wife just when I thought she might be with me?"

Isabel had been an honest girl and she was an honest woman. She knew the depth and intensity of her husband's devotion to her. There was no necessity for subterfuge here, even if she wished to conceal the nature of her errand.

She answered directly.

"I went to San Ignacio. I have been to confession to Father Claver."

Don Pedro d'Urbina was amazed by the avowal. But with the courtesy habitual to the Spaniard he did not upbraid his wife for something he could hardly be expected to approve. When he had somewhat recovered from his surprise, he said to her:

"My dear! How could you endure the company of the slaves in that miserable little hole, at the very time they were just back from the fields?" The thought of his wife, mingling with a crowd of sickly and unwashed Negroes, at a time the Jesuit Apostle had set aside to minister to their spiritual needs, was not a little disconcerting to the pride of the nobleman.

However, Don Pedro's voice was calm as he explained his feelings in the matter.

"I wonder, Isabel, you did not faint in that stuffy place. Of course, it is not the fault of the Father that things are not better. He has chosen the life of sacrifice. But you, my dear — I fear for your health. Would you care very much if I asked you not to go there again?"

As he spoke, Don Pedro d'Urbina noticed a paleness creeping over the perfect features of his beloved. Instantly he relented.

"Never mind!" he said, trying to speak gaily as he bent low to kiss the tip of Isabel's ear. "I won't interfere with your desires in the matter. Only, I shall be anxious lest you contract some disease from these visits. You know, Isabel, many of the Negroes working in the silver mines have bad lungs. Please, please, always take some preventive lotion with you if you must visit the chapel at that hour. Perhaps it would be well for you to take something now. I'm anxious. I'll find Jeromina and see what she thinks."

Isabel breathed more freely when her husband had left the room. She would take the medicine willingly, since Pedro wished it, for that was infinitely better than being deprived of something that had come into her life as a very breath of heaven. But, by the time he returned to the room, accompanied by Jeromina, who bore a potion of balsamic cordial, Isabel had gone to the front of the house to look through the grilled windows common to every Spanish residence in Cartagena.

Across the way the stoutly lintelled and pilastered doors of the mansion of Don Diego de Villegas gleamed in the sunshine as if studded with rubies and garnets. Far and near the bell towers, the arches in the garden walls, the turrets and bastions seemed engaged in tranquil meditation. The tall mata-raton bushes quivered in the breezes from the Caribbean and the stainless flowers of the tumbapared nodded their starry heads as if a band of white-veiled novices bowed at the Sacred Name: "Jesucristo."

Isabel was not noticing these things. She was thinking faraway thoughts. She was visualizing another city, a city of her native Spain; watching the sheep and goats grazing in the verdant meadows of Catalonia and looking on fields of millet and rye and dim groves of orange and lime trees. She was remembering another woman, a young Catalan mother, who had watched her only child go from her, never to return.

Had that mother regretted the oblation made to God even before her son was given to her, a priceless treasure, when the hour of sacrifice came?

But no. Spanish women never took back the things they gave. Pride, if not a white holiness, forbade it. The young Catalan mother had made the supreme offering with no regrets. Of that Isabel d'Urbina was certain.

Far from the little town of Verdú, behind granite walls washed by the ever-restless Caribbean, Ana Sabocana's young Saint had found his lifework, caring for the abandoned and outcast, the wretchedly poor and unhappy negro slaves.

Isabel thanked Ana Sabocana in the way she knew would be most acceptable — by a prayer to another Mother, who had sent her only Son to a horrible agony and death for the castaway slaves of sin.

"Ah! There you are, my dear!"

Don Pedro d'Urbina entered the room, followed by his sister-in-law.

Turning a smiling face toward them, Isabel extended her hand for the medicine her husband passed to her.

Chapter VII

FATHER PEDRO CLAVER had spent a profitable morning visiting the huts and sheds on the outskirts of Cartagena in order to satisfy himself that no aged, sick, or fugitive slaves were overlooked in his priestly ministrations. He had even penetrated the stables of several patrician families where his interpreters had told him he would be likely to find worthy objects of his zeal. When in the semidarkness he discerned a human form on a bed of musty rags or decayed rushes, he approached softly and spoke to the Negro with persuasive sweetness.

"Don't be afraid! I am your brother and I have come to make you a fine present."

That promise in itself was less important and appealing than the brotherly caress of the young Jesuit and the balm of his gentle presence.

Father Pedro had discovered a dozen forlorn blacks since leaving his confessional, where he had sat for several hours. He had wasted no time on his way to accomplish his mission. He had responded to the greetings of those who saluted him along the way with the simplicity and charm which revealed his twofold nobility, that of mind and soul, and that of blood. He had laid his hand in blessing on the heads of the little Spanish children who ran after him and held his faded habit. But he did not linger with them. He knew they were well cared for by those whose duties brought them in contact only with the agreeable side of life. His heart and his thoughts were with his slaves. If, occasionally, he paused beside the shop of a well-to-do tradesmen in the market place, it was only that he might solicit some little gift, to be bestowed where it would do great good.

The "fine present" the servant of Christ had to give the needy blacks was not a richly woven mantle or a sum of money or an easy task for which they would be amply repaid. It was the Faith of Jesus Christ, embracing all the good things of time and eternity.

Father Pedro loved his Blessed Lord so much that it was not difficult for him to bring others to his way of thinking. When he spoke to the forgotten blacks, lying in the desolate huts and shanties or in the slave warehouses outside the city walls; when he explained to them the articles of Faith, usually all who listened begged to be baptized. If Father Claver saw that the sick Negroes had not long to live, he would comply with their request, after he had given them the necessary instructions.

After he had poured the regenerating waters upon their foreheads he would smile happily. "Now you have my present!" he would say. "Try to take good care of it. I have given you the white robe of innocence. Never, never stain it! With it unsullied you will enter into the joy God has promised His faithful servants. Without it you cannot win heaven."

The Apostle knew that the Negroes were inclined to fickleness. He, therefore, took care to impress on their minds the thought that God punished evil as He rewarded good. He deemed it necessary to frighten the boldest of them, so that they would take the lesson to heart and keep their promises.

Father Claver never lost an opportunity of baptizing an aged or ailing Negro.

"Look, dear brother!" he would say. "The house is old and falling apart. It may tumble down when you least expect. Confess your sins! Make use of the opportunity God offers you. Do not cast it aside!"

Often those baptized by Father Claver were called away from earth soon afterward. As Father Morello had remarked to the Community: "It seems that heaven keeps many of these poor unwanted creatures alive until our young Apostle can reach them and give them the holy Viaticum. Not alone for their greater good, I think, but that Father Claver may have the joy and comfort that mean everything to him."

It was high noon when the Apostle of the Slaves passed down the Calle del Estanco, Street of the Tobacco Warehouses, on his way to the college. He was thinking of all he would like to do for his children in Christ. He wished that he might lead them into the open pasture lands of his beloved Catalonia and instruct them in those wide and verdant meadows. Beyond would stretch woodlands, cool and fragrant. Under the spreading dwarf palms, the limes and thorn-apple trees, he would arrange his beloved slaves in ranks, according as their instruction had progressed. Sheep would be feeding under the soft canopy of the Catalan sky where the floating clouds seemed as celestial flocks being led to the Fountains of Everlasting Waters. And he would tell his children in Christ of the Lamb of God who was led to execution without a murmur and who yielded up His life for poor abject slaves as well as for men of every other race and heritage.

There would no longer be need to beg at the doors along the Calle de la Media Luna or the Calle de Santo Domingo or any other patrician street for fruits and cooling drinks to comfort fever-parched lips. In the fields of Father Pedro's stainless boyhood was an abundance of all that heart or body could desire.

And the priest was thinking, too — for he was a practical man — that he would not deny his beloved charges a potion of the wine of Catalonia, rough and strong, but revivifying and strengthening when taken in moderation.

The servant of Christ was recalled from his reverie by the sound of his name.

"Father Pedro! Father Pedro!"

Turning, he recognized a slave boy, the property of a worthy citizen of Cartagena, Don Pedro Mercado.

The boy stated that his master desired to have the priest come at once to his house; his nephew, Francisco Lopez, had just died.

Father Claver followed the messenger. He walked past the Governor's Palace and the Inquisition; down the Calle de Santo Domingo and into the Calle de los Estribos, Street of the Coaches, where Pedro Mercado lived. Coming to the residence, he passed through the gate, over which hung a wealth of crimson acacias; their palm-shaped leaves reminded him of those spread before the Saviour upon His triumphal entry into Jerusalem.

He was at once ushered into the chamber where Francisco lay on a high canopied bed whose curtains had been drawn aside.

Francisco was known as a devout young man. It was his duty to collect the alms for the Confraternity of the Blessed Sacrament. Invariably he had chosen the middle of the day for his mission because when the sun's rays were most torrid he was more likely to find his patrons at home. He had gone out that day, as usual, but he had succumbed to the heat. On reaching home he had gone to bed. Soon after, he had apparently breathed his last.

"It happened very suddenly," Mercado said to Father

Claver. "We tried to persuade him not to go out today, because he had complained of feeling ill. But go he would, for he is a faithful lad. His imprudence has cost him — and us — dearly, Father. I always say that God does not expect us to endanger our lives in His service."

Mercado's voice broke on the words. He could not seem to continue in that fashion in the presence of Father Pedro.

The latter made no reply to the man's argument. When he spoke, his voice was quiet and confident.

"Francisco is not dead."

Immediately the others in the room rushed to the bedside. . . . The boy had not moved.

Father Claver spoke again.

"Our Lord, in whose service Francisco has lost his health, knows well how to restore it. He has permitted the danger to be so great in order to show the greatness of His mercy."

The priest then ordered that a certain kind of sponge be dipped in water and a little of this water squeezed into Francisco's mouth.

Mercado and his wife hastened to follow the prescription. No effect whatever resulted.

Distracted, the unhappy uncle hastened out of the house in search of Claver, who had left a moment before. Two blocks distant he came upon him. The Apostle was reciting his beads as he walked along.

"We followed your directions, Father," he said, between his sobs. "But Francisco did not move."

Claver spoke a little abruptly: "What!" he said. "Are you weeping in that manner for your nephew? Let us return to the house. Perhaps the remedy will succeed better the next time."

This time the priest asked that the water be brought to him before the sponge was immersed in it. When this was done he blessed it, stirred it with his right hand and administered a little of it to the prostrate Francisco.

miracle

The young man sighed heavily. Then he opened his eyes. Francisco Lopez was fully restored to health.

When the members of the household turned to thank Father Claver, they found him gone.

As a result of his charitable errand the priest was a little late in reaching San Ignacio. The Community had finished the noonday repast when he arrived. Silently he partook of a light collation of fried potatoes and corn mush.

Later, as the young religious was passing up the stairway leading to his cell his superior called him. Father Morello had something important to communicate to his spiritual son.

"Father," he began, "for six years now, you have been laboring for the Negroes here in Cartagena. I am convinced you have accomplished a good work in a spirit of obedience and charity. Now I am of the opinion you should prepare for your solemn profession. As you are aware, that act should inspire in you the absolute abandonment of everything that does not pertain purely to God and His holy service.

"It is my wish, Father, that you lay aside your external work for the time being and prepare for your final vows by a spiritual retreat of three days."

The young priest found himself unable to respond to this unexpected announcement. Watching him intently, Father Morello saw that he was troubled. He understood the reason. Claver's soul was so pure, so humble, so mortified that he considered himself unprepared for this step. But he was cheered by the Superior's words:

"At the close of your retreat and after your holy profession you will be free to return to your work for the slaves."

The heavenly light that shone in the eyes of the young priest amply repaid Father Morello for his kindness.

That night, when millions of stars glowed over the queenly city by the Caribbean and the bats hung lifeless, upside down, in the patio of the college, Pedro Claver knelt in rapt meditation on the principle and foundation of the spiritual life as expounded by his blessed Father, Ignacio de Loyola.

"El hombre es criado para alabar, hacer reverencia y servir a Dios nuestro Señor, y mediante esto salvar su anima; y las otras cosas la haz de la tierra son criadas para el hombre, y para que le ayuden en la prosecucion del fin para que es criado. . . ."

"Man was created to praise, reverence and serve God our Lord, and thereby to save his soul. The other things on the face of the earth were created for man's sake, to help him in the fulfillment of the end for which he was created. . . .

"Dedonde de sigue. . . ."

"Hence it follows. . . ."

Outside the windows of the humble chamber vagrant breezes stirred the fragrance in flower-starred streets and lanes. Romance, adventure, mystery lurked on every side. The heavy thickets of icaco surrounding the walls nearest the college hedged in the blue pellucid sea, whose creamy surf washed their base clear of all pollution. The old white town gleamed in the moonlight between its towering palms and rose-violet gardens.

No unwieldy treasure ship from Spain blotted out the distant horizon or churned the tropical sea water as it warily shoved toward the piers. No macaw sailed dizzily past, crying in raucous notes to the night, and the ibises, that in the early morning would come to take their stand on the yellow masonry, were missing.

Loveliest of all was Cartagenita, Little Cartagena, on a night like this. Or, as some of the people called it, El Corralito de Piedras, Corral of Stones, from the vast walls that shrouded it securely from the outer world. Only where the great trees swayed beneath the weight of monstrous creepers that gripped their trunks like straining arms, did shadows fall.

Had the young retreatant looked just then on the caimito tree it would have furnished him with a theme for meditation, emphasizing the contrast between souls in God's grace, crystal clear, and souls smudged and darkened by sin. For the leaves of the caimito were fair and shining on the upper side, but on the reverse dark and without luster.

When he had finished his meditation and made his prayerful resolution, Father Claver took up very tenderly, as if it were some delicately lovely thing, the crown he had woven from the thorns of the icaco bush. He pressed it, with fingers bruised and roughened by toil for his slaves, upon the head a saintly Catalan mother had often cradled on her breast.

Then, in a voice so vibrant with pain and yearning that it penetrated the adjoining chamber and was plainly heard by Father José d'Urbina, its occupant, he cried:

"Lord, why art Thou covered with wounds? Why is no part of Thy sacred Body without a bruise? Thy thirst for souls caused Thee to suffer so cruelly. How, then, can my heart remain insensible to Thee? Why do I not resolve to sacrifice myself for Thy love and for the love of the souls dear to Thee!

"Enough, my God, of the indifference in which I have lived up to this time; enough time have I lost in useless occupations while I could have worked for the conversion of the slaves! In future I shall not be so ungrateful. I shall devote myself wholly to their salvation. I shall preach Thy Name without ceasing. I shall become Thy slave, a slave of the slaves, since Thou hast not refused to be the Slave of men."

During the retreat Father Claver carefully consulted with his spiritual father regarding the perpetual dedication he wished to make of himself to the service of the negro slaves. The enlightened director accorded him permission to add to the usual formulae a separate simple vow of devotion to that effect. Superiors approved of this, and so, following the pronouncement of his solemn profession, Claver concluded his oblation with these words:

"Wishing to employ in a useful manner the remaining days of my life, I promise, O my God, to devote myself to the service of the slaves, sacrificing all for the healing of their moral ailments and the alleviation of their physical sufferings."

Father Pedro Claver, professed religious of the Society of Jesus, of the Province of New Granada in the Indies, signed his name to the formal declaration:

"Petrus Claver, Aethiopum Semper Servus."

"Pedro Claver, Slave of the Slaves Forever."

Part II

Tropical Noonday

Chapter I

IN THE PARLOR of the College of San Ignacio the Father Superior was conversing with Captain Juan de San Martin, whose ship had recently come into port from Cadiz. In honor of his guest Father Morello had brought out a bottle of very ripe wine, a gift from another seafaring man who had passed that way. The Jesuit himself partook sparingly of the wine; not so his guest.

The captain was in rare good humor for his voyage had been highly successful. Now he was to have the privilege of delivering a message to one of the fathers attached to San Ignacio. The message had been entrusted to him by a relative of the priest in Spain.

Father Morello regretted he could not summon Father Claver to the parlor. The Apostle of the Negroes, he informed San Martin, was conducting a missionary tour in the country districts of New Granada and would not return for several days. It was his custom to visit those of his slaves who had been taken by their masters into more remote parts, in order to minister to them, to encourage them to fidelity in the practice of their Faith and to give them the Sacraments. It was not in the generous heart of the priest to forget those whom he had instructed and received into the fold of Christ. But if the captain desired to entrust the message to him he would gladly deliver it.

San Martin keenly regretted Claver's absence. He had heard of his missionary work and entertained a lively curiosity concerning a nobleman who had forsaken all to undertake an apostolate so difficult and — so the captain deemed it — humiliating.

The next best thing was to entrust the message to the superior and ask him to convey the captain's regrets to the priest, with his ardent hope that when next the Santa Teresa made that port he would have better luck in fulfilling his mission.

The captain was thoroughly informed on the subject of slavery. He needed only the impetus furnished by the superior's allusion to Father Claver's labors to cause him to launch into a lengthy account of the practice as it had existed from the beginning along the shores of the Dark Continent.

The Jesuit found the account far from dull. The captain possessed an engaging manner and his facts were presented in a most entertaining way.

"It is generally believed, and reasonably so," said San Martin, "that the practice of making slaves of the Negroes had its beginnings in the first visits of the Portuguese to Africa. The Portuguese had in mind only the thought of material gain, and that very inordinate. The Moors at Arguin soon found themselves masters of a thriving business, since frequently from four to sixteen Portuguese ships came into that gulf.

"These ships were strongly fortified with arms. Their masters would land under cover of darkness and enter the villages of the native fisher folk. They would seize many of the Arabs and convey them to Spain where the unfortunates were sold to the highest bidder."

After the settlement of America, San Martin stated, this outrageous traffic had greatly increased.

"The Spaniards soon found that the Indians whom they

forced to labor in their mines and fields were not as well fitted by nature and physical qualities for that work as were the African blacks. . . ." Here Captain San Martin helped himself to another draught of wine.

"As soon as our people discovered that fact they commenced the importation of slaves from the Portuguese settlements on the Guinea Coast into Hispaniola."

The Jesuit questioned one point in the captain's relation.

"I was of the opinion that slavery was carried on in Africa before the Portuguese pirates appeared in those parts," he said. "Is it not true that the natives engaged in the traffic among themselves?"

"There is no doubt of it, Father. I meant to say that the Portuguese were the first Europeans to penetrate that section and open the commerce of the slaves. Soon the Spaniards, the French, and the English followed their example."

San Martin was well versed in the methods employed by the white men to entrap the blacks. He explained that it was the custom to collect the slaves by several methods, all of which were equally abominable to God and man. They were collected for transport directly by the Europeans or a middleman system was used; in the latter the captives were sold by black masters to the whites.

"The Europeans often send their boats to the different villages located beside creeks and rivers or by the seashore; or, they apply to the local factories, large ships stationed on the coast. In these stationary ships the poor wretches are confined until the vessels of the Europeans come alongside and the bargains are made."

The distance the captives were made to travel from the place of capture to the factories was often as great as twelve hundred miles, San Martin affirmed. Naturally, many spoke in such isolated dialects that not even the interpreters kept for that purpose by the slave owners could understand their speech.

"What is the purchase price of these blacks from the far interior?" the priest asked.

"Probably, Father, slaves of this description can be bought for no more than the worth of an ordinary pistol or sword. The buyers sustain a certain loss in the transaction. They must drive their purchases through the various small territories of local kings; for that privilege they are required to pay tribute.

"There are three distinct classes of slave traders who work from the interior to the coast. The class I have just mentioned is the most prosperous and important. Another class consists of those who travel inland but have no regular route of commerce or communication with the far interior settlements of blacks. When these traders manage to dispose of one lot of slaves they strike for another part of the shore. They make it a point to stop at all fairs and villages and from time to time go down to the shore to deposit their gains, human flesh. Later they return to seek further cargo. These traders are constantly going to and fro and have, as I said, no regular route or place of abode.

"There is, also, a third class of black traders. They go up the large rivers in canoes, each canoe thoroughly equipped with arms and carrying from fifty to seventy men. Often they proceed to a distance of one thousand miles. When they return they bring with them from sixty to one hundred twenty slaves at a time. The traders who go to the great markets or fairs in search of slaves generally spend about nine days on their quest. When they return they have with them from fifteen hundred to two thousand slaves."

The Father Superior mentioned the medium of exchange passing between the traders and the Europeans who took the slaves off their hands.

Cowries, or small shells, were in great favor for this purpose. On certain parts of the coast these passed for money. Romals, bandanoes, and other cloth stuffs of the Orient; muskets, powder, swords and liquors, were also used.

"Strings of beads are highly favored," San Martin continued. "Each section of the coast must have a different medium of exchange. The Africans, like the whites, often become tired of one thing and wish to discard it for something else. The kind and color of bead in favor one year is discarded the next. Sometimes red is the preferred color, sometimes green, sometimes yellow. This is also true of the shape of the bead. At one time the opaque is preferred to the transparent, the round to the oblong, and so on."

"I suppose we can hardly imagine the sufferings of mind and body the kidnapped blacks endure from the time of their seizure," the priest remarked. "Although he has never spoken of it, I believe our Father Claver often has great difficulty in overcoming the brutalized instincts of those who have been so cruelly treated."

San Martin nodded. "The captive Negroes often spend the greater part of a year traveling through the forests or across the rivers of the interior — this they must do to reach the coast. At the end of these journeys they may have to wait, shut up like caged beasts in the factories, until the ships of the Europeans come for them.

"Ships have been known to remain fourteen months on the Windward Coast, the territory extending from Cape Mount to Cape Palmas, before cargoes are completed and the slave ships ready to sail. When black traders in the interior of this territory have slaves to sell they signify that fact by keeping fires aglow. When the ships come that way and see the fires the slave traders investigate and accomplish their very profitable transactions."

In his turn Captain San Martin was privileged to hear the Jesuit's account of the negro trade in the Indies. The latter could give a vivid description of their lives and labors; much that he had not previously known had been told to him by Father Pedro Claver.

At best the Negroes had a miserable existence. "Of course, Captain, conditions differ according to the types of owners into whose hands the slaves fall. Generally the Negroes working in the fields are aroused at five o'clock in the morning to begin their work. Some cultivate the crops, others gather grass for the cattle. Of the two employments the latter is more burdensome and monotonous for the grass may be gathered only blade by blade. When a sufficiently large bundle has been plucked it must be carried a great distance from the plantation. The slaves are fed twice daily but the intermission allowed for the repast is very brief.

"After the second meal they are again set to work and continue at their posts until nine o'clock at night. Therefore, these Negroes must spend sixteen hours daily in drudgery. When at last they return to their little huts, worn out in spirit and body, they must attend to their necessary concerns before turning in for the night. Only five hours are allotted to sleep. According to the season, these hours are sometimes reduced to three and one half."

If a slave did not appear in his place on the minute assigned; if he was ill or exhausted; if he appeared to lag or his bundle of grass seemed small in the eyes of an unfeeling overseer the whip was laid unsparingly on his bare shoulders. That whip was so constructed that it would strip off the skin of the unfortunate victim, cutting out small portions of the flesh at every stroke. The Apostle of the Negroes, Father Pedro Claver, had frequently anointed the horrible wounds made in the operation known as slitting the ears, a punishment inflicted for a trivial or even fancied offence. Often it was imposed merely as a brand whereby the master could readily identify his property.

Father Claver was frequently called upon to persuade the tormented creatures not to run away from their masters, for it was certain that if they did they would be found and severely chastised.

Sometimes the owner of a remote plantation in the hills would come upon a fugitive Negro hiding in his fields. With diabolical cunning he would force him to labor for his interests, threatening, if he refused, to send him back to his master. The runaway would consent and would labor until the harvest was over. Then, totally disregarding his promise, the treacherous mountaineer would send the black man, loaded in chains, to his master and receive a liberal reward for his dastardly act.

"There is no need to speculate on what happens after that," the Superior remarked.

The interview at an end, both men rose and walked to the entrance of the college. Captain Juan de San Martin examined with some amusement the pictures of the early Jesuits on the walls. Some reminded him of pirates more than of priests, but the captain knew that the art of reproducing the human countenance on paper was not always successfully accomplished.

Some day, he thought, another likeness would be added to the collection, that of Father Pedro Claver. San Martin believed that the Spanish noble, now in the prime of manhood, was already a Saint. For had not Don Augustin Ugarta, former inquisitor of Cartagena, afterward Bishop of Quito, deposed that he had personally witnessed such acts of charity and mortification performed by Claver as had astounded and humbled him to the dust! Hearing that the priest was on his way to confess a Negro suffering from a contagious sickness and consumed by the desire to know more of the heroic missionary, the Inquisitor had followed him at a little distance. Don Augustin had even entered the negroes' quarters and placed himself in a position where he could watch all that went on without being seen.

The distinguished ecclesiastic came forth from the wretched place confounded and abashed. The sight he had witnessed brought home to him, as never before, the realization of the vast chasm that lay between mediocrity and holiness.

Not to be outdone by Don Augustin, whose story was carried through the city with amazing rapidity, the Archdeacon of Cartagena related an incident he deemed no less extraordinary and edifying than that recounted by his friend.

The archdeacon was accustomed to visit San Lazaro Hospital to distribute alms to the lepers. Going there on a certain day he found Father Claver in the midst of the sick. His face shone brightly and a circle of light was about his head. . . .

The august visitor had fallen on his knees, determined to remain in that posture until Claver had finished his work, then follow him and venerate his hand. But, although he had not permitted his eyes to leave the Apostle's face, it seemed that the latter sensed his presence. When his tasks were fulfilled Claver immediately disappeared, leaving the place by another entrance.

Captain San Martin would give anything he possessed to be permitted to do what was denied the dignitary of the Church — to kneel at Claver's feet and venerate, not the hands, but the very alpargates that bound the feet of the servant of Christ.

The captain had spent his life from earliest youth riding the Spanish Main. In his stalwart ship he had conveyed the rarest merchandise from the cities of the homeland to New Granada to adorn the houses and persons of the affluent Spaniards in the New World. He believed he had seen all there was of glory and beauty of earth, sea, and sky. . . . But now, as he passed along the weathered cloisters, empty save for a couple of pigeons holding conclave amid the arches, he was thinking of the Pearl of Pearls enshrined here in the Queen City of the Caribes. A saintly religious, who in a few hours would come forth, when the rest of his Community were sleeping. Not to sit in one of the tall-backed chairs in the upper gallery and comfort his frail body under the banana palms. But, like a pigeon, to flutter about the quiet cloisters under the pitying light of a young moon. "Bearing in his body the mortification of Christ," Pedro Claver would walk to and fro, his shoulders loaded with a heavy wooden cross, his brow encircled with a crown woven by his own hands from a thorny bush that flourished in the sands.

With a great love in his heart and a yearning prayer on his lips he would tread that Via Dolorosa until the first faint streaks of dawn, when the city gates were opened once more. Only then would he throw himself on his bed of hide to take the little sleep that would enable him to bear the burdens of another day.

In Cartagena of the Indies people talked much about those nightly vigils. And they said, one to another, that God would lovingly protect their city and its inhabitants while this angel kept guard over them.

Some such thought stirred in the soul of the debonair Captain Juan de San Martin as he passed down the street where the rose and blue had dimmed into orchid, thence to the soft gray of a dove's plumage. The dusk was setting as he reached his ship in the harbor.

Chapter II

HIS HOLY HABIT tucked carefully about his knees that he might better practice the virtue of poverty and do his task more effectively, the Father Minister of the College of San Ignacio was performing a twofold duty. He was sweeping out the corridor, taking care that the corners received the same attention as the more prominent spaces, and he was meditating on certain words applicable to his sublime vocation:

"*Serva regulam tuam et regula servabit te.*" Serve the rule and it will serve you.

Father Pedro Claver — for he now held the post of Minister as well as that of Master of Novices — was of the opinion that he served his rule very badly, although his brethren hardly held the same.

As Minister, Claver had charge of the brothers. He almost envied them their position which rendered them especially dear to Him who had been the willing Servitor of all.

He had tried to plead his utter unfitness for this special office. The Superior had turned a deaf ear to his representation. Always perfectly obedient, Claver had assumed his new duties with docility and resignation.

There was much work to be done by the few brothers. It often happened that a heavy burden fell upon certain ones. In that event Father Pedro divided the tasks more equably or performed a part of them himself, in order to relieve those under pressure.

On this particular day the Apostle found an unexpected opportunity to practice brotherly love.

When he had made the little house as tidy as possible he went upstairs to visit a sick brother. In winning manner he encouraged the invalid to practice patience and submission and recommended himself to his prayers. He then returned downstairs and went into the church to pay a visit to his Blessed Lord. As usual he was armed with a large number of special petitions, most of which related to his colored children.

The day was the feast of San Ignacio de Loyola. Kneeling before the altar where he daily received heavenly consolations in his Mass — always offered at high noon — the thought of his youthful pilgrimage to Monserrat, a shrine dear to his holy Founder, came to him. Even at that far-back day the desire to serve God in His needy ones was strong in his soul; on reaching the town he had immediately inquired about the sick, for he had wished to visit and console them.

The Brother Sacristan was shuffling about, performing little offices about the tabernacle. Suddenly he swayed to one side and fell on the altar steps.

Hastening to him, Father Claver lifted the unconscious man to his shoulders, carried him into the college and upstairs to his bed. When he had administered restoratives he sat down beside him and recited his beads for the brother's spiritual and temporal needs, meanwhile fanning him with a palm leaf.

The cry of a vendor of plantains reached the ears of the priest. The thought of the fruit, somewhat resembling the banana but larger and less sweet, caused a slight faintness to come over him. But it was part of his nature to resist every inclination to favor his body. And the vendor of plantains passed beyond the house, innocent of the fact that she had given the servant of Christ the opportunity to practice one more act of mortification.

When the brother had sufficiently recovered, Father Pedro went to the patio where a group of his black neophytes were waiting. With a smile of affection, he joined them. Having seen to it that all were seated to the best advantage, he began his instruction in Christian Doctrine.

The Apostle was aware that his work was not approved by certain persons, among them one or two of his brethren in religious life. Some there were who accused him of practicing innovations; these, they contended, were unnecessary and devoid of effect. Others were jealous of the humble priest because of the reverence and affection in which the Cartageneans held him. He knew that the majority of the slave owners disapproved of his attentions to their "property." Don Emmanuel Lopez, who had been enlightened on this score a long time before by the Jesuit rector, was one exception. Don Pedro d'Urbina was another.

Nothing, however, troubled Father Pedro except his own failings, which he believed to be very great, and the sorrows of others. He continued his work in peace, knowing that the humble acceptance of trial would bring a blessing upon it.

Soon another office was imposed on him. He was made Master of Novices. In that function the fervent priest found a great opportunity of helping souls. In his discourses to these young Spaniards, Father Claver took care to impress on their minds the necessity of a love for prayer, profound humility, and obedience to the will of their superiors. In their notebooks they carried many of the counsels of their revered master, Claver. . . .

"If you wish your soul to dwell with Christ, to whom you have offered yourself, deliver it from the ties of worldly affections. Despise the allurement of earthly attractions, for then you will be able to rise to the heavenly mansions and to employ yourself in holy conversation with your Beloved, experiencing in this life a portion of the joys reserved for the blessed in eternity."

And: "The Divine Master taught that our soul is like a field which, when properly cultivated, yields excellent fruits, but which, neglected, produces only thorns. Just as, without the rain from the heavens for the fields no trees would be produced, so without prayer, which attracts abundant graces, would virtue fail to increase in the soul. As the roots give strength to the delicately perfumed flowers, so does humility develop and preserve in us the most precious virtues. Lacking humility, the principle of the Christian life is also lacking in us.

"When the sap does not circulate, the plants become sterile and die. Spiritual death is imminent for the religious who does not love obedience. This is the virtue that supports a good novice, who relaxes, little by little, if he does not practice it daily."

The Father Rector of the college had that day remarked to another father that it was easy to know the source of the great virtue exhibited by the novices of the Community. Father Claver gave them a shining example of its performance in his own fulfillment of every duty he exacted of them.

The people of Cartagena were well accustomed to the sight of the saintly priest, swinging down the road in front of his new charges, the latter garbed in their poorest garments and armed, each one, with a broom. Through the most public thoroughfares they would go, to the Hospital of San Sebastiano; down the Calle de los Coches, Street of the Coaches; past the Archbishop's Palace, through the Calle de Estanco, Street of the Tobacco Warehouses. At the juncture of these two last-named streets, the Apostle turned abruptly to the right and entered the extension of the Calle de Santo Domingo; here the hospital was located and here the sick Negroes were housed, in the midst of a great lack of every material comfort.

At first the young religious in Father Pedro's care, most of them not long away from their native Spain, had found their work extremely hard and distasteful. But as they watched their Father in God, whom they knew to be also of noble birth, they absorbed something of his rare humility and spirit of self-denial, so that, gradually, their dislike of this apostolate wore away. And if, sometimes, the old temptations returned, they had only to seek Father Claver and confide the trouble to him, to receive such heavenly strength and comfort that for a long time the difficulty would not again present itself.

Father Claver encouraged his young charges to perform willingly certain works which he himself had performed from the very beginning of his sojourn in Cartagena. This was to wash the clothing of the ulcerous slaves, meanwhile covering them with their religious cloaks; then, kneeling beside them, instruct them in the Faith and prepare them for the sacraments.

The little procession of novices led by the courageous Claver always created a deep impression in the city, especially on the shopkeepers whose establishments it passed on the way to San Sebastiano. The vendors of sweetmeats and fruits, the cloth merchants and others poked their heads from their doors, their eyes round with wonderment. For the novices, noble of countenance and demeanor, looked neither to left nor to right, but kept their eyes downcast, their lips moving in prayer. None needed to be told whither they were bound or on what sort of errand.

Sometimes, when the merchant on the corner discerned the little army approaching, he would pass the word to his neighbor, and so on, down the line. The ruse afforded time for the shopkeepers to hide their especially treasured wares, lest they should have to relinquish any portion of them — to the Lord — as Father Claver would put it. Yet when the priest had come up to the shop that was the object of his desire and lifted a dust-stained and haggard but always smiling face, he found only smiles in return — and the smuggled goods returned to their counters.

Perhaps some of the affluent ones were superstitious about refusing to give to a priest. But the principal reason that moved them to comply with his request was the look in the deep eyes that seemed to penetrate the very souls of those who would haggle with Christ.

The school children, too, were ravished by the procession of Father Claver's fine novices. Nothing could prevent them from darting from their seats when they appeared — for the children had eyes in the backs of their heads when Father Pedro was at hand, the teachers declared.

The little ones were not ordered back to their places nor was any reprimand addressed to them on these occasions. Children were not wont to be slapped or scolded in Cartagena of the Indies. They had been made conscious that the mild and gentle eyes of the Señor, Jesucristo, were upon them, and this helped to make them mild and gentle.

Chapter III

IN THE PATIO of the d'Urbina mansion Don Pedro d'Urbina, husband of Doña Isabel, was telling his father-in-law, Don Juan d'Estrada, of a recent happening that had set all Cartagena talking. Don Juan wore a shawl over his shoulders; he habitually complained of the cold, even in the warmest weather. Huddled in his great cane chair, he rested his head on a very thin hand. The health of the old grandee had occasioned grave anxiety in the household of late. The occasional visits of Father Claver to the house somewhat relieved any tension. But it was apparent that Don Juan was far from robust.

Don Pedro d'Urbina was still slim and erect, although nearly two decades had passed since his marriage. His face was very grave as he spoke of the incident that had caused scandal to all the city and of its pathetic sequence.

For some time a flood of spurious coins had been making regular appearance in Cartagena. In consequence, the residents had suffered no little inconvenience and discomfort. They were greatly relieved when the mystery was solved and the coins ceased to circulate.

A Spanish captain, under suspicion, was apprehended, found guilty of the offense and sentenced to be garrotted in the Plaza of the Inquisition. Generally, after a garrotting, the body of the unfortunate was burned on a funeral

pyre. The tragic punishment was inflicted in public, so
that the miserable affair aroused everyone to a high pitch
of excitement.

Don Pedro had taken pains to ensure that the details
of the execution should not be mentioned in the household, deeming it an unfit subject for the ears of delicately
bred ladies. He believed he could safely speak of the affair
to his father-in law and rely on his discretion not to repeat
what he had heard.

With several other Spanish gentlemen of Cartagena Don
Pedro had been summoned as witness to the execution.
But his impressions of the unfortunate affair, which would
otherwise have filled him with horror, were considerably
softened by something that had occurred at the time of
the execution.

"Just before the unfortunate man was sentenced, he sent
for Father Claver," Don Pedro began. "Of course, the Father
went to the prison at once. He spent considerable time
with the condemned captain and eventually so softened
his heart that he became a completely changed man. It
seems that the criminal had a little notebook and in it he
wrote that the day of his condemnation was the happiest
day of his life since it marked the beginning of his perfect
conversion."

Don Pedro was unaware that Father Claver had in his
possession at that moment the notebook in which the repentant sinner had written these words:

"This book belongs to the happiest man in the world.
Justice delivers his body to death, thereby to save his soul.
I beg him into whose hands this book may fall to recommend me to the divine mercy. I have sinned, O my God,
and deserve not one death, but a thousand. My sorrow is
that I cannot repent sufficiently to atone for my offenses
against Thee."

Don Pedro described the execution in detail. He was

unaware that his wife had entered the sitting room and was approaching the open door, so that she could hear every word spoken in the patio.

"It was a hard thing to watch, believe me, father. The affair was badly bungled. The rope placed about the culprit's neck was frail; at the first turn of the spike it broke.

"Immediately Father Claver, who was holding his crucifix close to the victim's face, ran to press him to his bosom. At that very moment the executioner was trying to pass a second rope about the captain's neck. A religious in the crowd cried out that the priest should not have approached the criminal in that manner, that it was an extremely irregular proceeding. Father Claver remained unmoved at what was said. He only cried out, in a loud voice: "Be it so, if at this price I can help a soul! But, no! An act of charity cannot be irregular!"

Up to this point in her husband's narration Isabel d'Urbina had stood transfixed with horror on the threshold. Now the frightened expression of her face changed into one of serenity and confidence. The account portrayed the Apostle of Cartagena in a role so selfless, so compassionate, so Christlike in piety and holy zeal that he seemed more divine than human.

"I trust the miserable affair was speedily consummated!" Don Juan said in a feeble voice, drawing the shawl more closely about his shoulders.

"Unhappily, it was not," Don Pedro answered. "The second rope also broke. Father Claver repeated his charitable ministrations. It must have cost him much, for by this time the condemned man's color and expression were ghastly to behold. Far from fainting at the sight of so hideous a spectacle he remained close to the captain, praying and exhorting him to confide in the mercy of his Saviour. I must confess, I was obliged to turn my eyes away, several times, as the frightful experiments of the executioner were going on. Our esteemed neighbor, Don Augustin Barona, had to leave the spot.

"At last the unhappy affair was consummated. As they were preparing the funeral pyre, with the dead body lying face downward on the ground, Father Claver passed through the crowd. His forehead was dripping with sweat, but his face shone like a burning lamp. His eyes were downcast and he was praying. As he passed, the religious who had criticized him a few moments before, said, reverently:

"There is a truly religious man, who teaches us how to become so!"

Don Pedro d'Urbina would have been startled and amazed had he known that in a short time Father Claver would foretell the exact day of the proximate death of Don Augustin Barona, witness to the execution of the Spanish captain, although then apparently in perfect health.

Doña Isabel passed to her husband's side and laid her hand on his shoulder.

Don Pedro looked up, quickly. An expression of compassion not unmixed with discomfiture passed over his countenance.

In even tones he inquired whether his wife had heard much or all of his story.

Isabel had heard all.

"I regret it," her husband said. "These things are not for ladies' ears. I would not have — "

The nobleman did not finish his sentence. His minute scrutiny of Isabel's face revealed that, while she had found a part of the recital harrowing in the extreme, the rest had brought her a measure of happiness. Father Claver's heroism and the conversion of the poor counterfeiter were alike highly pleasing to God. Don Pedro sensed his wife's feelings in the matter and dropped the subject.

Seeing that Isabel was pensive, and that Don Juan had

fallen asleep, he drew her to him and passed his arm about her waist.

"I don't want you to think of these things, Isabel," he said. "Remember, you have one who is a part of you, who thinks of you always, most of all when he is forced to be separated from you." Don Pedro did not add that to a man who truly loved a woman, fields of sugar cane soon lost their semblance of beauty and the brilliant foliage and feathery tufts, waving like pampas in the breeze, grew infinitely wearisome. Then came the desire to be with the beloved.

"I think of you, Isabel, when I am riding along roads bright as gold and trade winds are tapping the leaves on the trees and gossiping in the bushes. . . ."

Isabel d'Urbina was amazed at the speech — her husband was not given to fine imagery.

She did not reply. Only she drew from its silver chain the medal of Nuestra Señora that hung about Don Pedro's neck and pressed it to her lips.

Chapter IV

ON THE GREAT WALL of the city near the foot of the Calle de la Media Luna jeweled lizards ran to and fro. A brilliant-plumaged cerraja, hummingbird of the tropics, poised for an instant on the yellow granite; then, frightened by the approach of a chain of negro slaves, spread its gorgeous wings and sped away.

Naked to their waists, their ebony chests and shoulders gleaming with sweat, the Negroes toiled to lift into place enormous blocks of granite. Beside them walked an overseer, whip in hand, ready to strike should any of the black men falter in their task.

From the Convent of La Popa, straining far out to sea on its lofty pine-clad hill; from the Convents of San Augustin and Santa Clara and from all the other bell towers in Cartagena sweet insistent voices began calling to one another. No sooner had they trembled into a deep silence than came another sound — the cry of a youthful water seller, leading his donkey and swaying to and fro in the rhythm of the cumbia. The docile beast dragged a little cart on two huge wheels; on the cart rested a water barrel painted a crude blue.

"Agua–a–a–" "Water!"

The cry penetrated within the d'Urbina mansion. It echoed in the stately sitting room, opening, as did all the rooms on the lower floor, on the patio. In this room Doña Isabel and Jeromina were busily sewing.

The cry of the little water seller, who wore a flor de la habaña, rose-colored flower of the tropics, in his purple shirt reminded Isabel that the day was very hot and humid. Setting her work aside for the moment, she clapped her hands.

In a moment the slave girl, Liseta, appeared.

"Liseta, bring coconuts and a sweet cake for the Señorita Jeromina and myself."

When the girl reappeared she bore a silver tray on which rested two green coconuts, rich in milk, and a portion of panela, unrefined sugar, fashioned into a small cake and wrapped in banana leaves.

When the ladies had refreshed themselves they began to converse in soft liquid tones of their native Spain. They spoke of the needlework done by the daughters of Santa Teresa of Avila in their cloister on the Calle de Santa Teresa; of the progress made on the great wall of Cartagena; of the health of their beloved father, Don Juan d'Estrada. Lastly, they spoke of their childhood home; of Sevilla, meandering along the banks of the lazy Guadalquivir River; of its sunny hillsides and its perennial suggestion of being enveloped in a mantilla of ghostly lichen; of the shops in the Calle de las Sierpes, Street of the Serpents, exotic bazaars where one could procure silk shawls as fine as cobwebs and elaborately wrought tortoise-shell combs.

Doña Isabel d'Urbina looked contentedly about the spacious high-ceilinged room, whose furnishings had been brought from Sevilla. The latter consisted of a couch covered with rich wool damask, several chairs and stools with leather seats and backs painted in bright colors and a large, richly carved, cedar table. A full-sized oil painting of the master of the house, Don Pedro d'Urbina, occupied the place of honor above the mantle; beside it hung a miniature of his wife. Several fine tapestries were disposed about the walls.

Isabel's thoughtful gaze rested on one of these tapestries. It depicted a holiday group coming from the Great Fair at Sevilla when, after the somber ceremonies of Holy Week, an air of gaiety everywhere prevailed. Beneath it were a few pieces of finely moulded blue pottery and ceramic tiles, whose soft glow was the result of a secret process none but the maker would ever know.

The sisters were expecting Father Pedro Claver any moment. The Apostle was on his way to visit Don Juan d'Estrada, to bring him the consolations of his holy Faith.

When he appeared, Isabel and Jeromina greeted him reverently, then knelt to receive his blessing. As he made a great Sign of the Cross over them, they repeated in unison:

"*Por la senal de la Santa Cruz, de nuestros enemigos libra nos Señor Dios nuestro. En el nombre del Padre, y del Hijo, y del Éspiritu Santo. Amen.*" "By the Sign of the Cross deliver us from our enemies, O Lord. In the name of the Father, and of the Son, and of the Holy Ghost. Amen."

Rising, both ladies waited for their revered friend to speak to them on his return from the sickroom.

Today Father Pedro had no message of reassurance in regard to Don Juan. Instead, he looked intently at the gowns on which Isabel and Jeromina had been working.

"My children, there will be no need of fine dresses here," he said.

The sisters were filled with dismay at the words. Something in the Apostle's expression caused them to refrain from asking an explanation of his meaning.

A month passed.

Each day a doctor called to see Don Juan. Several times

during the week Father Claver visited his old friend, to prepare his gallant soul for its Maker. However, he said nothing about administering the last sacraments.

"Your father is in no immediate danger," the doctor had said to Isabel.

She was not fully satisfied with the verdict, however. When she spoke of it to Don Pedro, he advised her to consult Father Claver.

She was well satisfied to follow the advice. But when, after confession, she asked her spiritual guide whether it might not be a wise precaution to administer the holy Viaticum to Don Juan, he assured her that it was not yet time.

Several days passed. At the end of that period the old man was seized with a violent attack of nausea. Everyone in the household felt that the end was near.

Doña Isabel immediately summoned her chair bearers and bade them take her to the Jesuit chapel. She felt certain Father Claver would be there at that hour.

The Apostle was in his confessional. When Isabel told him of her fears, asking his prayers for her intention, he struck his hand on the table before the tribunal.

"What!" he said. "Prayers for that holy Job! God has a brilliant crown in heaven for him — but not before Holy Week."

Isabel did not doubt her confessor's word. Her former mistrust and fear was turned into joy that her father had found favor with God and would soon be eternally happy.

Isabel was never to forget the scene attending the deathbed of the faithful Christian and chivalrous gentleman, Don Juan d'Estrada.

Father Claver administered the last sacraments in Holy Week. When the sacred rites were over he remained a long time by the bedside of the dying man.

The day was one of the most uncomfortable the rainy

season afforded. Each time Isabel approached the door, which was slightly ajar, Don Juan was talking volubly. Father Claver knelt beside him, reciting his beads; he must have wished to depart to fulfill other duties — he never spent time uselessly. In the present instance he remained by the bedside in order to consol his long-time friend by the balm of his presence and his prayers.

The nobleman, soon to leave this earth, was absent-mindedly speaking of the past; of the days when, attired in long cape and soft rolling brimmed hat he had gone to attend the fireworks exhibition for His Honor the Mayor, at Valencia. . . . His thoughts wandered a little, for in another moment they returned to his adopted country, New Granada. With eyes flashing and hands nervously picking the coverlet, he enacted the role of the chivalrous high-minded Francisco César, Don Pedro de Heredia's lieutenant, whose name was given to the river upon whose banks he had perished.

Doña Isabel, listening outside the chamber, knew how all-important these souvenirs were to him who recalled them on the verge of eternity.

On the one hand, there was the Divine Saviour, expiring on a cross for the salvation of the world, uttering His final words: "Into Thy hands I commend My Spirit," as the Apostle of Cartagena came to the third sorrowful mystery of the rosary. And Father Pedro besought, most lovingly, the dying Victim to give to the soul of Don Juan d'Estrada every help and comfort in his extremity.

On the other hand, there were the Indian inhabitants of a little village attacking the Spanish intruders fiercely, and a battle raging for two hours.

To Isabel it did not seem strange that her father's mind traveled in far-off channels at the hour of death. For the Spanish of Cartagena lived always in the remembrance of eternity. Their religion was the breath of their bodies and the life of their souls. Life, more than death, was a preparation for the next world.

Father Claver understood this even better than did his spiritual daughter. And she knew that he did.

Don Juan d'Estrada died peacefully on Palm Sunday, revered and mourned by all in the city.

Chapter V

A FEW WEEKS after the passing of Don Juan d'Estrada a solemn conclave was in session in the family circle. Doña Carmen d'Estrada, Isabel's sister-in-law, had come with her husband to the mansion on the Calle de la Media Luna to discuss an important matter.

The d'Estradas had three sons, the eldest named Isidoro, and it was concerning this boy that his parents sought advice.

"You know, Isabel," Carmen was saying, "I would gladly give my three sons to the Church if I felt they had the call. But I don't think that is true of Isidoro. He is an impetuous boy, easily discouraged and ready to give up an undertaking if it offers the least resistance to his plans. His father and I know his weakness. Now he is determined to become a religious. We can't forbid him to enter the monastery, but we believe his decision is the result of a passing whim. Actually, he . . ." Here Doña Carmen paused.

Don Lopez d'Estrada was not so delicate about disclosing the root of Isidoro's trouble as was his wife.

"Isidoro failed in his studies," he said. "I corrected him several times for his negligence in preparing for his classes. I thought him ready to do better. But yesterday his professor punished him for failure in a certain subject. So, home he came, his books packed under his arm, and announced to his mother that he intended to enter the

Monastery of San Francisco. Naturally, Carmen was astonished, for the boy had never previously broached the subject. She questioned him closely but could gain no satisfaction. He was bent on carrying out his intention. When his mother told me of it, I declared myself opposed to it. I don't believe Isidoro has a vocation."

Isabel d'Urbina reflected earnestly on what she had heard. She found it impossible to visualize the temperamental Isidoro as a friar. For one thing, the boy was overfond of fine dress.

"Isidoro apparently thinks of the Franciscans only because the Jesuits have found him wanting," she said. "He may be acting in a fit of pique. If I were you, Carmen, I would see Father Claver and tell him your story. Then, follow his counsel. He will advise you rightly."

Doña d'Estrada was fully satisfied to do this. She left immediately, accompanied by her husband.

When the two had gone Isabel reflected for a while on certain happenings in Cartagena in which Father Claver was intimately concerned.

The previous week she had gone to his confessional and had acquainted him with the state of her soul. She had received the sacramental absolution which never failed to bring wonderful peace and quiet to her woman's heart. Before leaving the feet of her confessor, something extraordinary had occurred.

The Apostle said to her: "Pray much for that poor martyr! Pray for him!" He repeated the injunction several times.

Under Father Claver's inspired direction Isabel had learned to curb her natural curiosity. She did not ask him to enlighten her on the subject of the "poor martyr." But she did pray often and earnestly for that needy soul.

A short time later Isabel received word that one of her

slaves had perished in a dungeon, with no human being at hand to succor him.

Feeling indisposed, the Negro had laid down his work in the fields and withdrawn to a spot where he might rest. The overseer immediately credited his act to laziness and insubordination. He ordered that the black man be punished with stripes, then locked up.

The order was carried out, but in a few hours the slave expired.

When she learned the horrid details of this affair, Doña Isabel knew that the slave had departed this life on the very day and at the very hour when Father Claver had spoken of him in the confessional, calling him "that poor martyr."

Since that time Isabel had recited, daily, the Litany of the Holy Name of Jesus for the repose of the Negro's soul, dwelling especially on the beautiful invocations that seemed most applicable to the persecuted blacks:

"Jesús nuestro Refugio; Jesús Padre de los pobres . . . tened piedad de nosotros!" "Jesus, our Refuge; Jesus, Father of the poor, have pity on us!"

Upon reaching the College of San Ignacio, Doña Carmen d'Estrada and her husband found Father Claver at home. When the priest appeared before them he was wearing an old canvas habit reserved for occasions when, after a begging tour, he was ready to visit the quarters of the sick slaves. He did not apologize for his appearance, but saluted his visitors with: *"Bendito Dios!"* "Blessed be God!"

After hearing the story the couple had to tell he said:

"Don't be alarmed! Isidoro will never become a religious. But you must make up your minds to consecrate to God your two younger sons, who will become Jesuits."

Astounded at the words, Carmen and Lopez thanked Father Pedro and returned home.

They found Isidoro still adamant. Nothing they could do or say could dissuade him from carrying out his intention of entering the Franciscan Monastery. This he did soon afterward.

Doña Carmen d'Estrada had said that neither she nor her husband would oppose a legitimate vocation for their sons. But now, when the two younger boys spoke of their desire to become Jesuits, Don Lopez violently opposed them. The youths followed Father Claver's advice; they waited patiently, praying for the favor they so eagerly desired.

After a month, Isidoro returned from the Franciscans. His father, anxious lest the headstrong boy should fall into mischief with time at his disposal, decided to send him to the island of Santa Catalina to transact some business for him.

Isidoro rejoiced at the opportunity of making a sea voyage. He embarked on the Spanish ship, *La Capitana,* and had a successful passage to the island. However, when the vessel had entered port, a false move on the part of the pilot sent her directly against a reef. As she was a frail ship she was completely destroyed.

The report of the catastrophe soon reached Cartagena. It was believed that all on board the vessel had perished.

The College of San Ignacio was soon surrounded by the sorrowing and excited relatives of those who had sailed on the ill-fated *La Capitana.* Among the first to reach Father Claver was the mother of the pilot. Her sole thought was for her son's salvation.

"Father!" she begged. "Tell me what has happened to my son! Only you know whether he is still alive. Tell me, Father, if he was saved!"

"Calm yourself, my child," the Apostle replied. "Only the ship was lost. No one on board perished."

Scarcely had the rejoicing woman gone on her way to

spread the glad tidings than Doña Carmen d'Estrada arrived. She was certain her beloved Isidoro had gone down with the ship. She came only to ask the prayers of Father Claver for the repose of his soul and for the courage she sorely needed to enable her to bear the trial.

Like the mother of the ship's pilot, she was overwhelmed with joy and consolation when she heard what the priest had to say. Kneeling at his feet, she stooped low to raise the hem of his habit to her lips.

Father Claver quickly withdrew a few paces. But not before the Spanish matron had caught a glimpse of a foot bound tightly with cords beneath the straps of the tattered alpargates.

Carmen arose at once. She knew that she had intruded where only Christ Crucified was welcome.

She wanted to thank the Apostle for this assurance. But words failed her as they had failed the mother of the pilot.

She was struck at the same moment by a thought that had never come home to her as now. The saintly man before her, whom her sister, Isabel, had often described as he was in his young priesthood, a frail youth whose illustrious origin and brilliant talents could not be concealed by the poor garments he wore — this youth, now a priest for nearly a quarter of a century, had sadly altered in appearance. His face was chiseled with many fine lines, the marks of sufferings and privations of every kind; his hands were hardened and discolored by rude unremitting toil; his shoulders were bent from many journeys through the city with heavy baskets loaded upon them.

Carmen thought that no one could look at Father Claver and not be better for having done so.

Up to this time the Apostle's consoling reassurance had not penetrated far. Cartagena presented an aspect of mourning as relatives and friends of those missing awaited the news they feared would be the worst. While Father Claver was attending to his visitors within the college, the Church of San Ignacio was filled with weeping men and women. Among them was Don Lopez d'Estrada. He had passed almost the entire day in the venerable place. Although his wife had told him what Father Claver had said he felt no sense of comfort or security. He believed God was punishing him for his refusal to allow his younger sons to enter the Society of Jesus. Stunned by anxiety and remorse, he now offered them without reserve to God. No sooner had he done this than peace filled his hitherto unquiet heart. This feeling increased as he left the church and proceeded homeward.

When he reached the house a slave handed him a paper. Glancing at it, he shouted for joy.

"Isidoro is safe! Isidoro is safe!" he cried, tears flowing freely down his cheeks.

At once he went to tell the good tidings to his wife.

"Father Claver told us so!" Carmen exclaimed triumphantly.

The sorrowing petitions of those who remained in the church were speedily changed to hymns of praise and thanksgiving. One of the Fathers attached to the college ascended the pulpit and preached a sermon suited to the occasion.

The Apostle of Cartagena was not present. He had gone to San Lazaro Hospital to "keep carnival" with his lepers.

A few days after this episode Don Lopez and Doña Carmen d'Estrada bade Godspeed to their two younger boys and sent them with a blessing to the novitiate of the Society of Jesus.

"Prepare yourself, my daughter, to receive a disagreeable piece of news in November," Father Claver said to Doña Isabel, as the latter was about to leave his confessional.

Isabel was not surprised, for these extraordinary statements had become more frequent of late. She went directly to the altar where she prayed fervently for strength to support the coming trial. She said nothing of it at home but went about her accustomed routine without undue anxiety or distress of mind.

Several days later the Apostle met Isabel and Jeromina in the street. Usually he did not stop to converse; this time he did so. His voice was filled with compassion as he said:

"About October! About October!"

October passed and no bad news had come to disrupt the peace of the household.

In November the Spanish fleet arrived at Cartagena. It brought melancholy news to the family of Don Lopez and Carmen d'Estrada as well as to Isabel d'Urbina and all the relatives of the family.

The young Isidoro d'Estrada, saved from shipwreck some time before, had reached Spain during the siege of Barcelona. Eager to take part in the combat and prove his courage and loyalty to the homeland, he had offered his services to the Spanish troops. They were accepted and he immediately went into action.

The dispatch that now reached New Granada stated that on the seventh day of the preceding month, October, Isidoro d'Estrada had died at the post of glory, joining the ranks of departed heroes of Spain. His death had occurred in the noble city of Barcelona.

In Cartagena, Doña Isabel d'Urbina went into the streets less often these days. Since the latest shipload of Negroes had brought a fearful pestilence into the city her husband had insisted that she take every precaution against infection. Because of this she refrained from visiting the Jesuit chapel although her heart was always in that spot endeared to her by holiest recollection.

Often she shut her eyes, that she might blot out the vision of rambling stone mansions with their flower-filled balconies and great bronze doors; the verdolaga and mangle trees that provided shelter and privacy for each costly dwelling. With her interior eyes Isabel saw the twin towers of the now remodeled and greatly enlarged San Ignacio, an architectural feature that served to set the old church apart from every other in the southern hemisphere. She saw the marigold side windows twinkling like so many jewels as they faced the sapphire sea. They reminded her of Castile and made her homesick. The stone that formed the eastern front had been brought from the far mountains of Turbaco. The houses of the Cartageneans hemmed in those massive walls as if they wished to come as close as possible to the sacred temple of God and so imbibe something of its holiness, its friendliness, and its peace. The color of the stone, a soft rich brown, reflected the solemn beauty of Caribbean sunsets, at times almost violent in their intensity, again softened into pastel hues as when a rainbow is fading on the horizon.

In spirit Isabel entered the high, grilled door to find sanctuary where, thousands of times, the pitiful feet of her Father in Christ went swiftly, noiselessly to and fro. She followed along the Moorish arches in cloisters cooled by the trade winds in the evening; into the chapel where Father Pedro daily offered the Holy Sacrifice at high noon — choosing that hour because he wished to fast as long as possible, and, too, because at that time no one would be likely to come seeking his help.

The soul of Doña Isabel traveled up the wide flight of stairs leading from the portery to the chamber of the man of God. It looked through the two windows keeping vigil above the strip of garden and the low wall the fathers had erected to shut off the premises from the sea. Those windows were other eyes, for through them the Slave of the

Slaves watched often and yearningly for the welcome sight
of a slave ship, coming into port. Straight as an arrow of the
Chibchas winging its way, the farseeing eyes of the Apostle,
which men saw so infrequently and women never, would
travel, travel. . . .

Perhaps, on the other side, Ana Sabocana looked out
and smiled at her loved one, and he smiled across at her
in the courage born of sacrifice.

Isabel wished she knew whether Ana Sabocana was still
living . . . if so, she must long to see her son. Or if, far
better, she looked down from heaven to watch her adored
Pedro, passing along the Calle de la Media Luna, to a
slave ship anchored in the harbor.

Chapter VI

THE REVEREND FATHER SUPERIOR of San Ignacio listened attentively while Father Pedro Claver spoke to him on a matter of the greatest importance to souls.

The Superior could study the face of his humble subject to excellent advantage since the younger man stood in his presence with eyes lowered. A slight flush brightened the cheeks of the Apostle of the Slaves. He deemed himself unworthy of the office he was about to request. Only an interior urge gave him the necessary courage to do so.

For several years English and Dutch pirates had swarmed, unmolested, over the Caribbean. Their comings and goings had occasioned no little concern to the officials and people of New Granada, who feared for the safety of their little kingdom and their homes. The audacious marauders had swooped down on two little islands, Saints Cristina and Catalina, belonging to the Spanish crown, and taken possession of them. They had established strongholds here and there on the islands and made them the point from which they sallied forth to pursue their evil traffic. No vessel was safe from them and lucky were the mariners on the high seas who escaped capture at their hands. Many ships laden with blacks, Mohammedans, and others had fallen prey to these pirates, who bore them off to their stolen islands and there forced them to cultivate the land.

When His Majesty the King learned these things he was

greatly disturbed. He quickly sent out a powerful fleet to war against the pirates. The commander, Don Fernando de Toledo, had orders to attack and conquer them. Fortunately he was successful in his efforts. In a bloody battle on the seas the Spanish emerged victorious. Those of the enemy who survived were taken prisoners and conveyed to Cartagena.

Don Fernando issued orders that the prisoners should be treated with due consideration. However, they were not to be allowed to go on shore. A strict guard was to be maintained over them at all times.

Father Claver was gravely concerned for the spiritual well-being of these captives. He was anxious to help them, but if he were to do so he must board the ships in which they were lodged. He now asked his superior to grant him the favor.

The Superior was edified by the Apostle's zeal and charity.

"You have my permission to board the ships and satisfy your desires, which are highly commendable," he said. "But you will first ask the commandant if this is agreeable to him. If it is — and I do not doubt it will be — you may proceed as you see fit. Under the circumstances I think it advisable to send two of the fathers with you; there will be plenty of work to be done."

When he had made the necessary preparations, Claver started for the harbor, accompanied by the two religious designated by the superior. The Apostle knew why the captives were detained on the ships; it was feared that if they were allowed to go ashore they would use their sharp eyes to ascertain the strength of the Spanish fortifications and would also spread their heretical doctrines abroad in the land.

One of his companions asked to be permitted to carry the sack in which Father Claver carried the requisites for the celebration of Mass on shipboard. A slight movement of the Apostle's head indicated that the request was denied. Yet the smile that parted the expressive lips told of his appreciation of the kind thought.

The two companion fathers walked behind, for the path was narrow. They conversed in low tones, while the commander of the little battalion sped over the ground as if his feet were winged. His brethren rejoiced with him; they knew how happy he was in anticipation of the good to result from the expedition. Father Claver carried the sack on his shoulder. Only Christ and His mortified disciple knew that it rested on a wide crimson stripe made by the discipline that very day.

The first ship the priest boarded held some six hundred prisoners. A little knot of Spanish officers stood guard over them. When these officers saw the Apostle, they cried out:

"It is the Saint! It is Father Claver!" Immediately they hastened forward to assist him and the other fathers on board.

When the captain appeared he bowed low to Father Pedro.

"We rejoice to welcome you, Father," he said. "We hope you will say Mass for us; we have been unable to hear Mass since we left the islands with our prisoners."

That was precisely what Father Claver intended to do, he assured the captain.

With the help of his companions he set up an altar and arranged it for the Holy Sacrifice. The Englishmen as well as the Spaniards drew as near to him as possible. With great respect they followed the sacred rites.

At the conclusion of the Mass the officers invited the religious to dine with them. Father Claver declined the honor for himself, saying that he wished to be seated with the prisoners in order to give them spiritual help.

The Englishmen watched Claver with some curiosity

as he said the grace before meals. They observed that he
ate almost nothing, and only the poorest portions of his
food.

When the meal was over, one of the prisoners, who had
been captivated by the courtly manners and grace of
Father Claver, said to him:

"Holy Father, we have our prelate on board with us. At
present he is resting in his cabin. Perhaps you would like
to speak with him. He is an important personage — the
Archdeacon of London."

Claver replied that he would consider himself highly
honored to meet the archdeacon. He believed that the
prelate had retired purposely when he learned that three
Jesuits had boarded the ship. However, this belief served
only to increase his desire to meet the Englishman.

When the two men visited the archdeacon's cabin, they
found it empty. Leaving Claver in the room, the officer
went in search of his distinguished countryman. In a few
moments he returned with the prelate, a man of venerable
appearance, with long gray beard and an amiable face
and manner.

The Jesuit and the ecclesiastic from London greeted one
another warmly. Soon they were engaged in animated
conversation.

The archdeacon questioned the priest concerning
Cartagena.

Father Claver gladly gave an account of that glorious
city, taking pains to include statistics of the work accomplished by the Jesuits in Cartagena for the Spanish and
Negroes.

After an hour's conversation the prelate introduced the
subject nearest to Claver's heart — religion. In the dis-
cussion that ensued the chief points of difference between
the Catholic and Protestant faiths were thoroughly
covered.

The archdeacon was astounded to find that every argument he advanced in defense of his religious beliefs was splintered by the keen lance of the Jesuit's frank and lucid, yet tactful replies. He remained lost in thought for some time after Father Claver had finished an eloquent exposition of the Church's stand on certain important matters.

At last the prelate was absolutely convinced that Claver was right.

However . . .

The crystal-clear gaze of the Apostle of Cartagena searched the crestfallen face of his adversary. Claver was now the master and the Englishman his disciple. He waited in prayerful suspense for the reaction of his new-made friend to his words.

"My dear Father, I am convinced of the truth of your arguments," the archdeacon finally said. "I honestly wish to embrace your religion, but a serious obstacle stands in my way."

Pressed by Father Claver for an explanation of his meaning, the prelate confessed:

"I am the father of a large family of children and I have a good and helpful wife. By means of my position I have been able to make a livelihood for them and for myself. If I accept your advice I shall deprive us all of our sole means of support."

The burning gaze of the Apostle continued to search the unhappy man before him. The archdeacon felt the strength of that glance and its secret power. In turn he looked into the face of the intrepid Jesuit. . . .

Claver was not a handsome man, the prelate decided. His features were not classic; his figure was short and somewhat stooped. Yet the whole man reflected strength of purpose, a lofty ambition and an interior and exterior grace, together with a purity and amiability that stamped his every movement and look.

The archdeacon glanced from his own well-kept hands to the hands of the priest, resting lightly on his knees. Although Claver held them palms downward the prelate saw that they were bruised and calloused. This frail little priest, of noble origin and talents, had made them so by his drudging labors for a despised and outcast race.

Never before had the Englishman been so moved. Yet he could not bring himself to go the whole way with God. He resolved on a certain compromise.

"I am sorry I cannot do what you ask, Father," he said, sadly. "But I can and will do this: from henceforth I will be a Catholic in heart, and Anglican only in practice. And I promise that at my death I will openly declare myself a Catholic and tell the real reason why I could not bring myself to do so before."

The archdeacon was disappointed to note that Father Claver did not seem satisfied with this declaration. On the contrary, it evidently displeased him.

When he spoke, it was to urge the prelate to think first of the salvation of his own soul and the souls of his family; to put aside the foresight that plans for temporal things and neglects the eternal. Claver encouraged and pleaded with the venerable man to put all his trust in Divine Providence, assuring him that God would not forsake him in his bitter trial but would grant him everything necessary to his happiness, here and hereafter.

The archdeacon listened patiently and sorrowfully. When Father Claver had finished, he only shook his head and repeated, mournfully, but firmly:

"I cannot do what you ask until the hour of my death."

A providential inspiration came to the priest. The day was the Feast of Saint Ursula, an English heroine of the Church. He now reminded the prelate of this fact.

"Sir! Today is a great day in your native land. A noble maiden, Saint Ursula, the glory of that land, is honored by the Church, which celebrates her feast day. With other virgins of England she shed her blood to confess the religion whose truth you yourself recognize.

"A king of Great Britain, Saint Lucien, sent magnificent gifts to the Holy See as proof of his devotion and allegiance to the Church. All the sovereigns of the Isle of Saints followed his example and continued the practice up to the time of Henry the Eighth."

The prelate lifted his head. He appeared less dejected than before. Father Claver realized that his plea had made an impression and he determined to follow it up with every argument he could summon to his aid.

He continued:

"It was Henry the Eighth who wrote in defense of the pontifical seat of Saint Peter. What could have induced him to abandon the Vicar of Christ and make himself supreme head of a local Church, cut off from the Church which Christ had built on Peter?

"Was not the reason the scandalous union he had contracted with Anne Boleyn, after having repudiated his legitimate wife?"

It was Augustine's argument against the Donatists whose application to the Anglican situation was to bring back so many others into the one and only universal, apostolic Church of Christ. As Claver proceeded the Archdeacon was fast becoming more profoundly moved. With that Claver addressed himself to the prelate in a more personal way. If he walked in the way of Henry and Elizabeth what could assure him that he should not die a death similar to that which closed the lives of both, even though outwardly less repulsive?

"Your possessions, your wife, your children — will they not then interfere with your conversion as they do at present?

"Be ashamed that you lack the courage to sacrifice your

possessions when youthful virgins gave their lives in sacrifice for God! Your first interest is that of your soul, your salvation. Do not expose yourself to eternal punishment for trifles you will soon have to sacrifice to others!"

Tears glistened in the eyes of the prelate as Father Claver concluded his argument. He was at last willing to accept the conditions of a wholehearted surrender of himself. Father Claver had won another soul for God.

The hour was late; the Apostle knew that he must return to the college for his other duties. As he bade farewell to his convert, the archdeacon gripped his hand. "Father, pray for me!" he said.

Claver promised he would do so. The two embraced one another and the priest went in search of his companions, who were awaiting him at the foot of the ship's ladder.

The sun was now rapidly declining and a fresh wind was sweeping inland from the sea. Again declining the offer of his companions to carry his sack, Father Claver walked before them. His heart was inundated with a peace and thankfulness too great for outward expression. The conquest of the archdeacon meant much to God, to the Church, to souls.

The convent bells were calling to one another; stealing in and out of narrow lanes and the dim recesses of the woods, they seemed to tell of joy and pain intermingled; of hope and solace woven with sacrifice. They counseled like a confessor, bidding men take heed to the things of eternity because those of time were passing. And when the things of time were swept away there would be silence, deep and lasting, in the tomb of the body that had long imprisoned the soul of man — a silence like that which settled over Cartagena of the Indies when the golden tongues ceased to call.

Father Pedro and his companions passed a stretch of deep woods, covered thickly with acacias so huge as to be almost trees. The Apostle had often taught his black children in these very thickets after having led them from the ships. Although the sweat dripped from his forehead, he did not wipe it away. The pieces of fine linen Doña Isabel had hoped he might use for himself, now secreted under his habit, would be used to cleanse the ulcerous wounds of some poor Negro; to wipe the blood and pus from cracked and feverish lips; to bind up the pathetic stub of a limb that leprosy was eating away.

The trade wind rustled among the leaves of the icaco, growing lush beside the path. The yellowish flowers were like so many wise little eyes looking after the man of God as he passed. In his heart he thanked God for them; they reminded him of that most beautiful of all cities, heaven, a city perfumed by the breath of God and lighted by His smile.

The three religious passed the confines of the acacia wood and came out beside a meadow starred with the violet of the campanula. . . . The weary Apostle remembered that the grace of God was like the trade wind that scattered the seeds of the campanula over the fields and woods, making of them a coverlet fit for a king . . . a carpet fit for the King of kings, whose hand had formed them and whose creatures they were, fulfilling His adorable will.

Chapter VII

IN HIS SUMPTUOUS QUARTERS in the government palace Don Pedro de Zapata, Governor of Cartagena, was conversing with the Consul, Don Francisco de Cavaillero, on a subject that caused both gentlemen acute distress of mind. The pestilence which had gravely alarmed the citizens, confining Doña Isabel and the other Spanish ladies to their homes for many days, was still raging. The officials were anxious to check it at its source — a slave ship lying at anchor in the bay.

The ship had come from the coasts of Biafra, its cargo destined to be sold and their services utilized in the mines and on the plantations. The plague had swept through the entire ship, having started in the hold where several hundred slaves were chained together.

The two officials could think of but one man in Cartagena who would not only be willing to board the infected vessel and tend the victims but would rejoice in the opportunity of so doing. Of that man they were now speaking.

"I have already requested Father Claver to perform so many acts of mercy for the unfortunate that I hesitate to impose this new task on him," the Governor declared. "Yet, unless someone goes to the aid of the sick Negroes they will die like dogs."

Don Francisco shook his head. "It is a thing neither you nor I nor any other ordinary mortal in Cartagena would undertake. In the first place, something more is needed than medicine and nourishing food to cure their bodies. Father Claver understands the Negroes and he enjoys their confidence and affection. A special Providence seems to be watching over this little priest, for it is not in human nature to labor and suffer as he does without exhausting the physical resources. Any other man would be in his grave in a month's time if he were to undertake a small part of the work Father Pedro performs. And he apparently does all this with as much satisfaction as the rest of us would feel were we to attend an exceptionally good Dialogue."

The governor relaxed. His face was less tense, for he visualized the solution of his problem.

"You have relieved my mind of a great burden, Excellency," he replied. "To a degree, I alone am responsible for the well-being of these Negroes. As you say — and I admit the truth of the statement — I am no more equal than you to aid them. Under the circumstances I must excuse myself from boarding that ship, for there is no special Providence over me! I am happy to think that Father Claver will help us. I shall ask him to call on me at once."

As soon as he received the Governor's summons Father Claver hastened to the palace. It required no persuasion on the part of Don Pedro de Zapata to induce him to undertake the dangerous commission. When he learned the nature of it, he smiled as happily as a novice who has received a word of commendation. He expressed his readiness to visit the ship at the earliest moment and minister to the plague victims.

Returning home, he donned his old canvas habit and, with a basket of fruit and medicines attached to his walking stick, set off at a rapid pace for the harbor. Along the way he stopped at several shops to add to his stock of supplies.

Ashamed of his own lack of moral courage, the Consul had ordered that the infected vessel be thoroughly fumigated, so that Father Claver might be safeguarded against contagion. The Governor had told the priest the nature of the disease — it was smallpox. When the fearful word was spoken Claver had neither recoiled nor shown any other indication of fear.

Don Francisco followed the Apostle as far as the upper deck of the ship to make certain his orders were carried out, quaking, to be sure, and holding a fine handkerchief, drenched with perfume, to his face. From a safe vantage he looked on as Father Claver went on his knees from one prostrate Negro to another, hearing the confessions of those who had been baptized and speaking to them in their own language when the services of an interpreter were not needed.

When he had done all he could for the souls and bodies of the victims, he ordered carts to be brought to the ship. The ailing Negroes were placed in them and taken to an empty slave pen on shore.

The Apostle, riding in one of the carts, reached the pen first. He assisted the sick into the miserable shack, cared for them according to their needs and received the newcomers as, one by one, other carts arrived.

He had not proceeded very far with this work when he realized that some of the Negroes spoke in tongues wholly unfamiliar to him.

There was but one person in all Cartagena who understood the principal Negro dialects. This was an old Negress, Magdalena Mendoza, one of Claver's converts. He determined to send for her and ask her to come to the ship and perform an act of charity for her needy countrymen.

Magdalena, when the emissary from the priest arrived, was sitting in the yard of her little home, in the shade of a giant bonga tree, drinking chicha, fermented maize, very sparingly, for she was a wise old woman. Grumbling a little, she agreed to go to the warehouse. She could not find it in her heart to refuse one who had been very kind to her; who had instructed and baptized her and given her the fine medal she wore about her neck. Before her meeting with the Apostle of Cartagena, Magdalena had been a faithful adherent of Mohammed, as so many of her people. Now all the treasure she desired was the string of brown berries fashioned into a rosary, which was always attached to her ample waist.

It was very comfortable in Magdalena's back yard and the tattered rope hammock in which she had expected to take a nap was a fine bed for any old black woman. But, at Father Pedro's call, she toddled off to the slave warehouse.

When Magdalena reached the door she peered cautiously in, for the light outside was so bright that by contrast the dim interior of the pen rendered her almost blind for the moment.

Soon she could see the Negroes lying about on the floor. In their midst was Father Pedro, supporting a youthful sufferer on his breast while he administered a medicinal drink to him.

The old Negress had often visited the premises, but never under circumstances such as this.

The men who carried on the unholy traffic in human flesh were usually utterly callous to the miserable plight of their property. The old and dilapidated houses into which the slaves were thrown on their arrival in Cartagena, and where those remained who were too ill to go on, were revolting in the extreme. Barren and dirty walls, a floor damp and strewn with refuse, a roof that leaked in every quarter greatly increased the sickness and mortality among the victims of the hideous system. One, or at most two, windows afforded scant light and ventilation to the dreary enclosure. When several hundred Negroes were huddled together in this unholy habitation the air speedily became foul and many quickly succumbed to its contagion. No distinction of sex or age was recognized, but all lay jammed together in abject misery. Young children often watched in wide-eyed horror the death throes of their parents, or of some aged Negro covered with ulcers as a result of long neglect and abuse by his godless master. Horrid cries and groans, mingled with curses, issued from the lips of those who cherished no hope here or hereafter, but who expected to end their unfortunate lives in the charnel house of despair.

Magdalena continued to watch for a few minutes, unobserved by either priest or Negroes.

Having finished his task with his young patient, Father Claver approached a venerable black man whose stark eyes revealed the frightful anguish that was consuming body and mind. Calling a couple of stalwart Negroes to his aid, the Apostle bade them lift up the aged man while he shook up the strands of old straw and bits of dirty matting that served as his bed. When this was done and the sufferer had been laid upon it Father Pedro directed the blacks to clean up the filthy place. Meanwhile, kneeling on the floor beside his patient, he tenderly washed the parched face with perfumed water.

Gradually a calmer and saner light crept into the swollen eyes of the old slave. With a wrinkled and bony hand he clung to Claver's habit, looking mutely into the pitying face of the servant of Christ.

Magdalena had held herself erect at the door of the slave pen until now. But, suddenly, overcome with repugnance and disgust for the filth within, she felt that she was about to swoon. Try as she would to conquer the weakness, she could not. A nose was a nose, even if not classical in outline, and cheeks were cheeks, even though the skin upon them was tough as the hide of an ox and adorned with sundry excrescences in the form of boils and pimples. It was another thing when the flesh was ravaged by hideous scars, beyond the power of any doctor to restore.

Magdalena turned abruptly and went a few paces down the shore. But not before Father Claver was aware of it.

Running to the door, he called to her in pleading voice: "Magdalena! In the Name of God, come back! These are our brothers, also! How can we abandon them and leave them without help?"

The sound of the loved voice restored the Negress' lost courage and confidence. She knew that the heart of her Good Father was filled with loving solicitude, not only for the stricken Negroes, but for her soul, which he had saved.

Filled with confusion over her desertion, the old woman obeyed her spiritual father like a child. She retraced her steps and calmly entered the slave pen, couragously giving her service until Father Claver's work was done.

Back in her favorite nook under the bonga tree and snugly ensconced in the old rope hammock, Father Pedro's best interpreter was now well satisfied with herself. A great peace rested on her aged heart. She no longer feared the fell disease. She, Magdalena Mendoza, an ugly old black woman, was, nevertheless, white and sparkling deep down inside. Father Pedro had seen to that, in his own inimitable way.

It was he who years ago had baptized her. Bedecked in a wonderfully clean gown of white cotton, made and donated by Doña Isabel d'Urbina, Magdalena had stood in the line of ten Negresses, all of whom Father Pedro had prepared for the solemn event. Very important did she feel as the sacred rites were consummated.

So that none of the newly baptized should forget their

saints' names, the Apostle had bestowed the same name on all the members of each group. Therefore, there were nine other Magdalenas in Cartagena of the Indies. Only one, however, was so highly privileged as to be the right hand of the Good Father in his work for the newly arrived slaves.

On that hallowed morning Magdalena had watched, wide-eyed, every gesture of the priest and listened to his every word. She recalled other occasions when Father Claver had striven, by his severe warning against evil-doing, to lead his spiritual flock to a higher path. Thus he had not minced words in explaining the significance of the painting, "The Last Judgment," which had greatly alarmed Magdalena before her conversion.

"Nay, but except ye repent, ye shall all likewise perish."

The old Negress had sacrificed much satisfaction in giving up attendance at the superstitious rite known as "Tears of the Dead," a highly immoral practice that inevitably ended in the commission of the most abominable sins. But her supreme sacrifice was made when she ceased to visit the groves and woods where the slaves indulged in their favorite dance, the cumbia.

Father Pedro had encountered his most difficult task when he endeavored to put an end to indulgence in this pastime.

The cumbia was thought to have originated in the region of the Congo. All the slaves were familiar with it. After the tropical sun had set, about half past eight at night, the black children of Cartagena assembled for an orgy of pleasure. Under a great sea moon that resembled a grotesque face looking down on them they began this terrible pastime which often brought its devotees to the verge of madness.

The first time Father Claver had witnessed the cumbia his soul was filled with horror, mingled with a great pity for the ignorant and superstitious Negroes who sought diversion from their woes in the only form of recreation they knew.

The light of the moon accentuated the ghastliness of the scene. The faces and bodies of the dancers were covered with many-colored paints and smeared over with sperm oil. Not unlike the motions of a rodeo the cumbia began, its participants gradually growing more excited and violent. Soon melancholy cries and chants issued from their lips; these grew wilder as the moments passed. At times the notes were modulated to sadness, resembling the wailing of infants; again, they resembled the protests of those under torture. The African gaita, a musical instrument like a bagpipe, gave forth a melody sometimes sweet, sometimes distressing to the ear, while the rumbling "tun, tun" of the drum could be heard far over the city, calling the Negroes to the grove. When the Spanish people heard it in the seclusion of their homes they said to one another: *"El ronquido de leon tropical!"* — which was to the effect that the drum was inviting all the riffraff of the neighborhood to hasten to the dance.

As the blacks hurried to respond to the welcome sound they would often stop and, bending down, lay an ear to the ground in order to hear the vibration of the weird music.

Usually a knot of spectators watched the contortions of the dancers. As this audience gradually increased, a circle five or six rows in depth looked on. These persons, who did not take actual part in the dance, carried lighted torches of sperm oil which gave to the trees and all the vegetation about an appearance of being aflame. The torches were indispensable on nights when there was no moon to penetrate the hidden recesses of the grove.

Everyone present joined in the primitive African chants, sometimes happy and innocent, sometimes profane. The

air was filled with a strange odor, the result of a mixture
of scented waters, flowers, tobacco, and alcohol that clung
to the bodies and scant garments of the dancers. Thinking
themselves the reincarnation of the souls of their ancestors,
they became more overwrought from moment to moment
until finally, frenzied, they began to throw off their clothing and, half naked, continued their profane rites.

In their chants they repeated the name of the dance
over and over. *Cum,* meaning drum, and *ia,* to move or
dance and make a loud noise — words of an African dialect — were joined to form the name, *cumbia.* These words
were sung with a pronounced guttural sound, the *i* very
long, a strong accent on the *a.* The *m* was guttural, also
the *b,* and came from the throat. Each of the two syllables
was pronounced very distinctly and blended admirably
with the movements of the body in the dance. So greatly
did the Negroes love this popular pastime that most of
them walked with a swaying movement. This was particularly true of the women in their homes.

Old Magdalena Mendoza, Father Claver's best interpreter, had ceased to visit the magical groves from the
time of her first meeting with the Apostle of Cartagena.
How wonderfully her faith and constancy were repaid
none knew as well as she who was so honored as to share
in the apostolate of her Good Father. She had been present
among the spectators on an unforgettable night when the
cumbia was in full swing. Something extraordinary had
occurred that night. It made a deep impression on Magdalena as on hundreds of others present in the grove.

The stars of Cartagena were twinkling over the tips
of the ceiba trees and the Caribbean moaned behind the
great sea wall as if keeping time to the music of the gaita
and the reed pipes when, suddenly, a "white spirit"
emerged from nowhere.

With a crucifix in his left hand and a short whip in his right, Father Pedro Claver had invaded the precincts of his archenemy, the devil. Holding the crucifix high over the whirling figures he had struck, not too gently, several of the Negroes, his converts, who, lapsing into their former superstition, were taking a leading part in the ghostly rites.

Frightened and abashed, the black men had shrunk back, the whites of their eyes showing in the starlight, their mouths hanging wide open in astonishment and dismay.

Father Claver had gone among the women, taking from them their dearly prized pagan emblems, bits of sticks crossed and arranged in a certain way on their breasts. In place of these he had given to each a cross which he had blessed, made of the wood of the poison tree, very slender and flexible. Magdalena's cross was even now affixed to the wall above her bed, a treasure prized beyond all her other possessions.

The musicians, Negroes who played on the reed pipes or the gaita or beat the drums for the dancers, had taken to their ebony-colored heels and disappeared in the forest. However, as Magdalena shrewdly surmised, they would not long elude the watchful Claver. At some future time they would lay down their instruments, forsake their abominations and turn to the loving Saviour, who must be very good since His servant, Father Pedro Claver, was so very good.

Chapter VIII

DOÑA CARMEN DE BADAJOS was relating to her friend, Doña Isabel d'Urbina, an incident that had greatly amused her during her recent visit to Sevilla. Carmen, who as a young girl had laughed at Father Claver's painting of the Last Judgment, had altered little in the years. A handsome and frivolous girl, as a woman she was most attractive and given to trifling. Isabel was dismayed to find her friend as irreligious as ever and her thoughts wholly centered on pleasure.

In Sevilla Carmen had attended the Goyesca, a procession in which the participants were costumed as characters from the paintings of the Spanish masters. At another time, wearing a gown, whose elegant bodice was almost concealed by a lace mantilla brought high over a jeweled comb, she had gone in triumph to the Sunday afternoon bullfight.

"You remember, Isabel — "

Isabel could only nod her head, a little sadly, in answer. The passing of that grand figure of the Spanish aristocracy, her beloved father, Don Juan d'Estrada, and the pestilence which the city had only recently thrown off, after heavy loss of life and serious discomfort to all classes, had reduced her to a pensive and anxious state of mind. She listened to Carmen's chatter, but with far less interest than of old.

The woman of the world had met an old friend of both ladies in the Alcazar Gardens. Beneath the famous equestrian statue of Hercules and Julius Caesar that had stood in the Alameda de Hercules for many years she had come upon this *amigo* of the olden days. Had she — ? Of course, she had not coquetted with him. But, putting the question the other way — that was a different matter.

"You are the same Carmen," Isabel said as she regarded her friend with an elder-sisterly look.

Carmen laughed hilariously. She read the unspoken thought in Isabel's mind. "For my part, I should not think of spending hours with my face hidden in a prayer book, as you do, my dear!" she remarked. "Not even when I am an old woman. Even then I intend to be captivating as well as beautiful!"

Carmen did not think it advisable to shock Isabel by speaking of something that had happened as her carriage was passing a certain corner in Sevilla. A priest was standing before a boot-boy's stall while his shoes were being shined. This priest had rebuked her and his look had reminded her of the look on a young Jesuit's face, long before, when he heard her mocking laughter in the Plaza of the Inquisition in Cartagena.

The priest in Sevilla was a much older man than the other had been; he had frowned as he noted her costume and had shaken his head in displeasure. However, this priest was in no way distinguished, she had decided, and it was not worth-while to pay attention to him.

Carmen did not mention Father Claver. Isabel, however, could not long remain silent on the subject nearest her heart.

Carmen knew what to expect. She waited, believing she would find the forthcoming confidence highly diverting.

Isabel was not loathe to speak. She had continued under Father Pedro's direction. Many of the Spanish of

Cartagena, including government officials, had done the same. At first Claver had demurred, fearing that too much time would be taken from his work for the slaves. But when it was represented to him that, by the direction of these souls, his influence for good would be greatly widened, he had consented.

When Isabel had finished speaking of Father Claver, Carmen bethought herself of something. She said nothing of it to her friend, but soon excused herself and went off in high spirits. In a few minutes she was at the door of the Jesuit chapel. Bidding her slaves wait, she entered the dark and ill-ventilated edifice.

The chapel was nearly filled, for several of the fathers were hearing confessions. Carmen found a place just inside the door, not far from Father Claver's confessional.

It appeared that the Apostle was in the tribunal, for she could hear the sound of muffled voices coming from that direction.

As the priest in Sevilla had told her, in his glance of grave displeasure, Carmen's dress was such that no modest Spanish lady would think of wearing it. Carmen herself was aware of this, but the knowledge only served to intensify her desire to attract as much attention as possible.

Noting several acquaintances near by, she began to whisper, freely, then to converse in tones loud enough to be heard by all around her. This disturbance and the rustling of the silk in her costume as she turned about, attracted attention in a way she had not foreseen.

Watching the devout prostrations of certain penitents before the altar, Carmen finally forgot herself and laughed aloud.

It was of no avail to stifle the outburst in a tiny web of lace. She feared lest she had aroused Father Claver — a thing she had no wish to do.

Her fears proved well justified.

The Apostle emerged from his confessional. With indignation showing in his usually calm face he spoke in tones that all in the church could hear.

"Señora," he said to Carmen, "your dress and conduct are very improper for the house of God, especially in the holy season. This is a time the Church has set apart to remember the sufferings and death of Jesus Christ. Why did you not think of this? Your behavior is most unseemly — and at your age!"

Carmen de Badajos was furious over the rebuke, particularly over the allusion to her age. She had never been trained to subdue her passions. Forgetting everything save her outraged feelings and the disgrace of being rebuked before so many people, she spoke insolently to the priest.

"How is it that you are so lacking in respect to a lady, sir?" she said. "It is plain to see that you are a forward, uneducated person. Your place is with the miserable slaves, not with those who have been delicately bred!"

The pitch of the offended lady's voice had ascended with her rage, so that the words could be plainly heard in the college, next door.

Father Claver was silent, waiting until the tirade should come to an end. Meanwhile, all in the church sat spellbound, amazed and disedified.

The Father Rector was walking outside the college cloisters, reading his office. He was startled and shocked to hear the furious outburst of Carmen.

From the Brother Sacristan, who had just emerged from the chapel, he learned its source.

At once he went to the scene.

Carmen was still screaming. She had lost all sense of propriety and self-control.

The Superior was wholly unused to incidents of this kind. He believed that the fury of the lady could be appeased in but one way. That way was a painful one, but he deemed it the only method of procedure under the circumstances.

Addressing Father Claver, he told him that he had been imprudent and lacking in discretion; that in future, when dealing with others, he must moderate his impetuosity and govern his impulses.

Carmen watched the Apostle intently. She had at first experienced malicious pleasure in the realization that her tormentor had been rebuked — however little he deserved it — in the presence of all. But now . . .

To her infinite surprise Father Claver offered no excuses to justify his conduct but behaved as one justly condemned.

Prostrating himself at the Superior's feet, he humbly begged his pardon and asked that he be given a severe penance to atone for the trouble he had caused.

The Superior could not bear to look into Claver's face. He dared not, for it had cost him much to rebuke in public one entirely innocent of blame, since he had acted with a pure intention, for God's glory and the good of souls.

The Apostle returned to his confessional, leaving everyone, including the guilty cause of all the trouble, stupefied. The exhibition of meekness and mortification they had just witnessed served to increase the love all cherished for the Apostle — all, except Carmen de Badajos.

As speedily as possible that lady made her way to the street. When she had hidden herself in the depths of her chair, she bade her slaves convey her —

"Anywhere!"

The black men were neophytes of the priest. They were horrified at what they had heard. Their mistress was silly and conceited — yes — but they had never known her to fly into such a passion as that of a few moments before.

The reason for the outbreak they could not guess. Only Father Claver had dared to tell Doña de Badajos what she deserved and needed to be told.

"Anywhere!" Carmen had ordered. But a moment later she issued explicit directions as to her destination.

"Take me to Magdalena's hut!"

Magdalena, she who had so nearly failed Father Pedro in his hour of need, was not far away.

In front of the hut Carmen descended, sweeping the sand with her elegant flounces. She entered, without knocking, the thatched-roofed dwelling which her mother, whose faithful slave Magdalena had been, had bestowed on the old woman for use during her declining days.

The mistress of the imposing establishment of one tiny room, boasting a single window and a balcony protruding like a bird cage into the street, was at home. She was squatting in her "garden," a mixture of seeds and weeds, with a few straggling flowers in every stage of bloom and decay.

Stiffly she rose and greeted the fine lady whom she would always call "Young Mistress." Then she waddled to a shelf and brought down a coconut, offering it to her guest after she had split it neatly open. She forbore to offer Carmen any of the chicha which reposed in a gourd near by.

Carmen, however, declined the refreshment. The Negress soon observed that something had upset the usually self-complacent worldling.

Long experience had taught the old woman that in dealing with the Spanish it was wise to refrain from commenting on their affairs, above all, from asking even the most innocent question.

The elegant visitor twisted a flower-laden vine that crept up to the door of the hut, as she inquired:

"What's the news in Cartagena, Magdalena?"

Wholly ignorant of the incident in the chapel, Magdalena launched into a vivid description of the baptism ceremony conducted by Father Claver only a few days before in the slave warehouse near the Baluarte de San

Antonio. The audience of one was very attentive as the Negress proceeded with her narrative.

Having arranged an altar where all could see it, Father Claver selected the godparents. As a convert in good standing, and a special helper of the Apostle, Magdalena was among them. Those selected were the most faithful and fervent of the black Christians Father Claver had baptized since his coming to Cartagena.

Close to the altar was a large painting of the Crucifixion. With many fervid gesticulations Magdalena described the figure of our Lord. His five wounds were streaming torrents of blood. This Precious Blood flowed into a baptismal font. A venerable priest, attired in rich vestments, poured some of it on the head of a kneeling Negro. Around the cross were illustrious personages — kings, emperors, and princes.

In the background of the painting, Magdalena said, was a group of Negroes wearing fine ornaments; these were the baptized Christians. But, at the other side — here the old woman shivered and covered her eyes with a withered hand — was a group of deformed Negroes, monstrous to behold, surrounded by demons. The latter were the obdurate blacks who had refused baptism, preferring to remain in their errors and superstitions.

Magdalena did not know that her guest had looked on a similar painting, by means of which Father Claver impressed the truths of the Faith on the minds of the slaves, and that she had made it a subject of ridicule.

Carmen, making no comment, sat on a board beneath a bonga tree, biting her lips, her cheeks a deep vermilion. She began to understand something of the meaning of Father Claver's life and work and the reason for the methods he employed in teaching the neglected and ill-used blacks. Only through sometimes starkest appeal to their imaginations could they be made to grasp the significance of the religion of Him who died on the cross for their salvation as well as for the salvation of the whitest men on earth.

Magdalena had not noticed the alteration in Carmen's demeanor. She continued her recital, greatly enjoying the role of storyteller.

After completing the arrangement of the altar, Father Claver placed those who were to be baptized in line, dividing them into two groups. The slaves in each group were to receive the same name in baptism, so that no one would forget his Christian title.

Then Father Pedro knelt before the painting and in a loving petition offered to Christ these souls redeemed by His Precious Blood, begging Him to grant them very special graces.

The women were baptized first, then the children and, lastly, the men.

Dropping on her knees before the astonished and uneasy Carmen, Magdalena re-enacted the role she had fulfilled in the preparation for her own baptism. As Father Claver had taught her to do, she folded her arms on her breast. At this point in the proceedings the Apostle had shown the baptismal water to his neophytes and said to them: (Here the bondswoman explained in her own words what Claver had said.)

"See, my children, the water of health! Through the merits of Christ it purifies the soul; it takes away all stain of sin and restores to us the state of innocence lost by our first parents.

"Here is the fountain of grace, that forms true children of God and gives them the right to His heavenly kingdom. But, if you wish it to have the same effect on you, you must detest your sins with all your heart and renounce the devil forever.

"And now, my children, do you wish to enter into the

fold of the true Church and receive holy Baptism?"

Father Claver had repeated these words several times, very slowly and distinctly, to make certain that he was clearly understood by all. He insisted that each neophyte should answer the questions put to him or to her in the affirmative and should show a lively desire to become a Christian. When all had done this he proceeded to the baptism ceremony, going through each part with great devotion.

At its conclusion the Good Father of the Negroes preached a sermon, warm and joyous and loving, the old woman said. When he ceased to speak, there was a joyful reunion. Father Pedro, surrounded by the newly baptized, received and returned their childlike attentions. He then went to a corner of the room and brought out several large baskets, loaded with delicacies. There were scented lotions that reminded one of the lovely flowers in the patios of Cartagena. There were oranges and mangoes, coconuts and bananas. There were fine white handkerchiefs, little wooden crosses and a medal for each new-made Christian. The medal was to be worn about the neck.

Carmen's face was somber as she remembered another who had part in this beautiful, wonderful thing. Isabel d'Urbina, her childhood friend, was privileged to share her devotion, her sympathy, her worldly goods with Father Claver for the propagation of his sublime work. Favored Isabel! Yes — and favored Magdalena!

More than an hour had passed and Carmen's chair was still in front of the hut. At the end of that time the lady rose, forgetting for the once to shake and brush her fine skirts. Something she had never done before she did now. She took the hand of the old Negress and pressed it between her own fair hands.

Lost in wonderment at this display of affection, Magdalena forgot to enlighten her august caller on a very important point. Namely, that, although there were just then nine others of her name in Cartagena, only one could boast the proud distinction of being the Father's very special interpreter. She did not think it necessary to mention the dubious incident of a certain day when Father Claver had called imploringly after a fleeing figure:

"Magdalena! Magdalena! Come back! For the love of God!"

The love of God and Father Claver could do anything at all in Cartagena of the Indies, the old woman believed.

When the faded eyes of the slave had watched the chair of Doña Carmen de Badajos disappearing in a cloud of sand, she remained standing at the door of her tiny home, looking up the street. The behavior of her visitor had aroused a great curiosity in the mind of Magdalena.

What had happened to bring about this change in Doña Carmen?

Chapter IX

FATHER PEDRO CLAVER was gathering up the little favors left on the table before his confessional — in which he had sat for several hours — when he saw the solicitor, Juan Sanchez, coming in at the chapel door.

The priest had often gone to Sanchez when he wished to obtain a favor for some Spaniard accused of a crime and condemned to die. The avarice of certain men in the city who were ready to sacrifice virtue and reputation for personal gain frequently brought innocent victims into the hands of the authorities. Father Pedro always seemed to know about these cases, even before others came to him to seek his intervention in their behalf.

Just now the Apostle was stiff and sore in body. The recent rains had greatly increased the dampness of the church and his confessional, being near the outer door, was the most unsanitary of all.

He had listened patiently to all kinds of miserable tales, most of which revealed the brutality of slave masters and overseers, but, also, the virtue, sometimes heroic, of his dear converts. He was constantly called upon to do his utmost to convince the Negroes that they must not run away when they found their burdens too oppressive. In the event that they failed to follow his counsels, they were inevitably brought back and subjected to cruel punishment. When Father Pedro knew that a runaway had been returned to his owner he immediately went to the latter to intercede for the culprit. Often his pleas won forgiveness for the poor bondsman, or at least a lightening of his penalty.

On this occasion the tired Apostle, taking care not to reveal his physical condition to his caller, accompanied Sanchez into the garden, overlooking the sea, and walked with him under the palms while he listened to his friend's story.

"I need your help, Father," the solicitor began. "A client of mine has had the ill luck to commit a homicide. It was premeditated, although I can truthfully say he was driven to it by desperate circumstances. Soon afterward he told me of it. Contrary to my advice, he left Cartagena and was proceeding into the interior when he was pursued by the authorities and captured. Now they can think of no penalties sufficiently harsh to impose on him."

Father Claver asked whether the man had received the death sentence. The reply was in the affirmative.

"You will come with me to the prison, Father?" Juan asked.

He had little need to put the question. Almost before he had ceased speaking Father Claver was hurrying across the garden and disappearing within the college. When he returned he had his old cloak on his shoulders and his walking staff in his hand.

Together they went to the prison. Sanchez remained in the corridor while Claver entered the cell of the condemned prisoner.

Diego Perez, the unfortunate murderer, was crouched on the cold stone floor, loaded with chains. His head was bowed in dejection and his whole attitude was one of black despair.

The priest knelt at his side. When he had embraced him he took the crucifix from his habit and placed it in Diego's hand.

The face of the condemned lost its hopeless expression as Father Claver said to him, in gentle tones:

"My poor child, men have condemned you without the possibility of redress. But God has not yet pronounced His final verdict. In His mercy He has reserved a great benefit for you. Have courage, my son! I come to offer you, in His Name, a plank for your salvation. Jesus, who shed His Blood and sacrificed His life on a hard cross, wants to pardon you. He is ready to say to you the words He spoke to the good thief on the Cross, provided you do not refuse His grace. He has been most merciful to men. He has instituted a wonderful Sacrament, by means of which we may reclothe ourselves with the white stole of innocence, even after we have fallen into the gravest of crimes. We can save ourselves if we grasp this holy plank firmly.

"My son — there is no way left for you to flee from the tempest. How happy I would be if I knew, as God makes it known to you, the day and hour of my death! Some go in advance; the steps of others are retarded. But sooner or later we must all see the thread of our life cut by the inexorable hand of death. We must all go into eternity!"

The Apostle forgot that he was tired and stiff of limb and that the cords binding his toes cut more deeply than usual. He remembered only that his was the sublime privilege of assisting a forlorn soul on its way to the Supreme Judge. His final words were whispered into the doomed man's ear as tenderly as a mother would whisper to her sick child.

"What do the things of earth matter then! Of what use is this world when it ends so soon! Let us think of saving our soul, because if it is once lost, it is lost forever."

By the time Claver had finished his exhortation Diego Perez was praying. Again embracing him, Father Pedro began the difficult task of helping him make a sincere confession of his whole life.

Although treating the wounds of the sinner very considerately, the enlightened confessor wished to give him every opportunity of doing penance before entering another world. He took from his habit a small scourge and handed it to Diego, telling him to apply it to his person a certain number of times.

Diego received the scourge humbly and respectfully. He felt happier when it was in his possession because he was convinced that his confessor had used it often upon himself.

When Father Claver emerged into the corridor he found Juan Sanchez anxiously waiting to learn the outcome of the visit. But the solicitor was no longer concerned when he saw the expression of his friend's face. It assured him that all was well with a once guilty soul and that God's grace and the Apostle's efforts had wrought a happy change.

The solicitor walked by Claver's side as the latter retraced his steps to the college. Juan was enthusiastic when he learned of a plan in the priest's mind.

The date of the condemned man's execution was not far distant. Father Claver proposed to be at the prison early that morning. He would assemble all the prisoners, including Diego Perez, in the chapel and would celebrate the Holy Sacrifice of the Mass for the man soon to die, and give him Holy Communion. Our Blessed Lady would come in for her share of homage; her litanies would be chanted by the prisoners in unison, Father Claver leading them. After that, the Apostle would address the men. The crucifix would be his sermon book, since, he affirmed, it could preach much more eloquently than he.

At the last, Claver would speak directly to the condemned man, urging him to renewed penitence and confidence in the mercy and goodness of God.

Juan Sanchez, the solicitor, had entered into many alliances with those who had fallen into the hands of the law. He had believed himself hardened by the unhappy experiences. Yet now he brushed away a tear, unashamed, as he listened to the Jesuit's account of the proposed services at the prison. He wondered a little — that a man could be so cheerful who had just prepared another man for a painful ignominious death. Then he remembered that without this spiritual conquest of a sinner, another human being would have gone into eternity unshriven and unmourned. Father Pedro's principal concern was eternity.

Sanchez registered a solemn resolution that nothing should prevent him from attending the ceremonies Claver described, and by his devotion and interest in the now repentant Perez, give proof of his loyalty to that holy Mother Church who so generously provides for even the weakest of her children.

Juan Sanchez was to live to a ripe old age. But he was never to forget the touching and impressive scene in the prison of Cartagena on the morning of the execution. He would cherish for always the heart-rending words of Claver to the motley collection of prisoners. But most of all he would cherish the memory of the Apostle, at the foot of the scaffold, one hour later.

Father Claver approached the man whose terrible mistake had brought him to an untimely and tragic end. With a piece of linen he wiped the sweat from Diego's forehead. His magnanimous heart rejoiced that his spiritual son had exhibited unusual bravery on the way to execution — he had marched straightforward, head erect and eyes steady, holding Claver's crucifix to his breast.

The final absolution was given by the hand that had purified and soothed so many poor sufferers in the long

years spent in Cartagena of the Indies. Bestowing a parting
embrace upon Diego, Claver spoke to him for the last time
in this world.

"My son," he said, "behold the ladder by which you
ascend to heaven! Kiss each step with love and respect
before placing your foot upon it. By it you approach nearer
to God, who waits to reward you for your tears of sincere
repentance."

Although some who stood by scoffed openly at the sight
of Diego fulfilling these counsels of Father Claver, Juan
Sanchez, the solicitor, wept, unashamed. He had hoped
that his client might be acquitted of the charge against
him because of the extraordinary provocation that had
brought about the crime. Now he felt that this was the
better ending of one man's life story. For none could go
from a sinful and troubled world better prepared to meet
his God than Diego Perez.

Father Claver, too, was deeply moved. He prayed in a
loud voice, without interruption, as the punishment began. When the executioner had finished his task and the
victim no longer breathed, he left the scene and retired
to the prison chapel to pray for the soul of the departed
murderer.

"May God grant us, also, the grace of weeping for our
sins as the good Diego wept for his!" he said to Sanchez,
who accompanied him to the door. "May we have a holy
death such as his!"

The Apostle denounced those who took pains to inform
on the prisoners in order to make their lot as hard as
possible. "May God forgive them! While it is certain that
they secured the death of that man, it is no less certain
that they are running the risk of losing their souls!"

"You will take a little rest, Father?" the solicitor begged,
although he felt the words were idle. The horrible hour
through which both men had passed, particularly the priest,

had been among the most trying of their lives. Sanchez could understand something of the pain it had caused the compassionate Claver to stand by and look, without yielding to his feelings, into the frightened eyes of Diego. The Spanish method of strangulation of that day, garrotting, allowed the victim to suffer a long-sustained agony. At first the rope was tightened only slightly, by the movement of a long stick inserted at the back of the neck and held at either end by an executioner. This served to paralyze the nervous system. Little by little the spike was moved in this manner until the penalty was paid in full.

During the prolonged and terrible punishment Father Claver had continued to look bravely into the eyes of the sufferer, seated above him on the scaffold, his hands tightly bound behind his back, the veins standing out in frightful manner on his empurpled face. When all was over the throat of the tortured priest was hot and dry, as if a fire had been kindled within it, searing every fiber and nerve.

Claver avowed that he had no need of rest. He was certain a few penitents would be waiting for him in the chapel. Therefore, he would go directly to his confessional.

In the chapel the Apostle found a small group of Negroes and one other, of whose presence he was not at first conscious.

A sound as of suppressed weeping reached his ear as he bent to hear, as he supposed, the confession of a slave.

He glanced quickly toward the penitent. His alert senses detected the odor of a perfume more costly than the scented waters the slaves loved to use. Only fine ladies of Cartagena used perfumes as subtle and delicate as this.

It was a Spanish noblewoman who sought comfort and counsel. At first it was difficult for the priest to learn what was troubling her, for she continued to sob for some moments.

Encouraged by Claver's kind words, the lady, Doña Carmen de Badajos, lifting her tear-drenched face, told him who she was and humbly begged his pardon for the scandal she had given in the church and for her insolence toward a servant of Christ, beloved of all the people.

In the dim light the penitent glanced timidly at her confessor. Father Claver had partially covered his face with his hand. Yet, even at that disadvantage, Carmen thought she had never before seen a look of such surpassing beauty on a human countenance.

When Claver spoke, it was to thank God for having brought this erring child to Him, after so long a time. Discreetly, but with the thoroughness characteristic of everything he did, he helped the once proud and worldly woman over the difficult places in her confession. Then, with a lingering Sign of the Cross and in a voice of greatest fervor and unction he imparted the sacramental absolution.

Carmen thanked her confessor and was about to rise when he detained her. He wished to give her a few counsels to help her to persevere in her new resolutions.

In order to accomplish the will of God, he reminded her, men and women must despise their own wills, since the more one died to self, the more one could live in the Lord. The more the heart was purified from pride, the more would the love of God come to fill the soul. One ought never lose peace, no matter how strong the trials of the day might be.

Carmen de Badajos had never heard such sweet words spoken in so sweet a manner in all her gay and carefree life. She remained on her knees, breathless, silent, taking care not to allow her thoughts to wander for an instant from the immediate present. She wanted to remember always what Father Claver was saying to her, Carmen de Badajos, as if there was no other needy soul in all creation — on the happiest day of her life.

Like the quiet ripple of a caño, a stream or backwater in a wood, the quiet voice spoke on.

"We must remain silent in contradictions and in the corrections we are asked to endure without cause."

At the words, Carmen's cheeks grew hot. She recalled how her confessor had himself remained silent in the face of a cruel reprimand, administered in that same little chapel, and her own shocking behavior to one whom she now recognized as a Saint of God.

She dared not tell the priest that she was sorry for the undeserved rebuke she had brought upon him. For had he not just told her that this was the very thing one should most desire, for the love of God?

"To make great progress in virtue, we must exercise great care in the control of our tongue," Father Claver was saying. "Our words ought to be adorned with peace, with truth and with the praise of others."

Doña Carmen de Badajos would dry her tears in a short time as, gradually, the peace of her conversion quieted her once storm-tossed soul. And she would laugh again, in silvery peals, at the lively repartee of her friends, or the piquancy of a Dialogue when, with others of the sex, she would attend that popular recreation.

But she would never again laugh at Father Claver's painting of "The Last Judgment."

Chapter X

AFTER HIS PENITENT had left the sacred tribunal her confessor remained for some time in the same position, communing with his Lord. His heart was steeped in joy and thanksgiving for the conversion of this soul. He had not dared hope for it; in his simplicity and low esteem of himself he had not imagined that his edifying behavior in the face of his Superior's reprimand had anything to do with the Lady Carmen's change of heart. Had such a thought entered his mind he would instantly have repudiated it and done penance for it.

The maxims Father Claver had given his new penitent were his own, for he had made them so by long practice. But the spirit of them he had received from his revered teacher and guide, Brother Alfonso Rodriguez. So, now in memory, the soul of Pedro Claver went out through the low door of the chapel, across the sandy street, past the flower-garlanded balconies and the brisk little shops whose doors were tightly closed and shutters drawn in the mid-afternoon heat. It ascended to the decks of a great ship, about to leave the docks of Cartagena of the Indies and sail across the mighty deep. To Majorca it would sail where, again, Alfonso waited for his disciple.

Then — the Apostle of the Slaves remembered.

Alfonso would not be there, exercising his lowly duties as portero at the Jesuit College of Palma. For Alfonso had gone home to God and his place was empty.

From the city of the proudest cloth merchants of Spain, Segovia, whose weaves were the finest in all the world; from that city whose stately streets had lately flowed in rivulets of blood in the uprising of the Communeros; whose many beautiful churches and convents had stamped the seal of God across its borders, had come this marvelous man.

Alfonso Rodriguez had once lived the life of a happily married man and father of a family. But when those nearest and dearest to him had been taken by death, he had entered the Society of Jesus as a lay brother. Everyone in the College of Palma knew the judgment passed on his extraordinary vocation by the father who examined it:

"I have had a talk with Alfonso and examined carefully into his life and purpose, and I feel obliged to admit him as a Saint, for I intend that he shall be one. He will give great glory to the Society by his virtues and example."

In the providence of God this "Saint" had pointed the way to the young Pedro Claver, his disciple at Majorca, to an heroic apostolate in the New World.

Claver was just twenty-five years old when he arrived at Palma on November 11, 1604. As soon as he entered the college he sought out the holy lay brother, whose reputation for sanctity had spread far. As if by mutual instinct the aged religious and the young student embraced one another with reverence and affection.

Pedro Claver had begged permission to speak with Brother Alfonso for half an hour daily on the affairs of his soul. The request was granted. Humbly, thankfully, Alfonso received the treasure entrusted to his keeping; in so doing he was guided by an interior obedience. From that time on, the young Claver had made swift progress on the path of divine love, profiting by the guidance of his saintly friend.

Alfonso had seen in vision the thrones of the elect. One was empty. He was told that that one was reserved for his beloved pupil, Claver, as a reward for his distinguished virtues and labors and the multitude of souls he would win in America.

The saintly brother had not told Claver of the vision. Only to his confessor did he mention it, and the latter made it known only when he deemed it time to do so.

Father Claver, however, knew of an incident related by Father Vincent de Arcaina, professor at the College of Palma. As that father was standing one day at the door with Brother Alfonso, the latter asked him:

"Who are those two coming through the courtyard, about fifteen paces off?"

Father Vincent replied that they were Brothers Pedro Claver and Juan Humanes. Then Brother Alfonso had said:

"Those brothers will go to the Indies and will there reap great fruit for souls."

Although Claver was just entering the college at the time and Alfonso Rodriguez had not as yet met him, the prediction came true. Claver was to labor until death in Cartagena, while Juan was to find his field of apostolate in Paraguay.

On another occasion Alfonso had said to one of the fathers, as he pointed to Claver:

"Do you see that young religious over there? He will go to the West Indies, where he will accomplish great work for souls and he will reap immense benefits from his mission."

Later, and directly to young Pedro himself, Alfonso had spoken of his yearning desire to see missionaries go out to distant lands, to conquer souls for Christ.

"My dear brother, I cannot express in words all the pain I feel when I think that God is unknown to the great majority of men, because in many regions His ministers are lacking. We ought to weep at the thought of the many countries that are being lost because there is no one to save them; that perish, not because the inhabitants desire it, but because no efforts are made to reach them.

"We find so many useless workers where there is no harvest; where there is an abundance of it, the workers are few. What a multitude of souls they would send to heaven if many European priests, now living in culpable leisure, would go to America! But they avoid the difficulties of such a voyage and do not fear the responsibility of abandoning those souls. The riches of those regions are eagerly sought, but their inhabitants are despised!"

When Alfonso had aroused Claver to an eager interest in the missions of the West Indies, he went a step further.

"Cannot charity cross those seas which greed has been crossing for so many years?" he pleaded. "Many vessels arrive at the port of Spain, loaded with treasures, and how few souls arrive at the port of a blessed eternity! Why is the world more desirous of accumulating riches than sharing the love of Jesus Christ through the conquest of souls? However savage these needy people are, they are precious jewels, whose price would be returned many times to those who would undergo the labor of polishing them.

"O, my brother, son of my soul! What a vast field for your zeal! If the glory of God interests you, go to the West Indies. Go, to save thousands and thousands of souls that perish! If you love Jesus Christ, go and gather His blood, shed for the benefit of nations ignorant of its value! Labor for Him until death, for the salvation of men, as you belong to His society!"

Much more had the holy brother said to the youth until the heart of Pedro Claver was fired with the desire to dedicate himself to the service of the Negro slaves in distant America. . . .

The death of the servant of Christ was as his life had been, hidden and lowly. Alfonso Rodriguez lay very ill. His superior had told him that he had worked as long as he was able to work and that he must take a well-deserved rest.

Winter came, and the college was very cold, for the funds were meager and a stout fire could not often be kindled when the harsh winds blew from the sea.

Brother Alfonso was lying on the bare boards of his bedstead. The infirmarian had forgotten to come and unroll his mattress. In the early dawn this brother came in to visit his patient.

Although stiff with cold and weary after a night of pain and discomfort the aged religious had smiled.

"I have spent the night to my heart's content," he said. "I shall soon be well, thanks to the Lord!"

Soon . . . soon . . . Alfonso had been well. So well that there would never be anything more for him to suffer in this world. His heavenly birthday had arrived when he was in the eighty-sixth year of his age.

Sitting cramped in his little confessional in the now empty chapel in Cartagena, Pedro Claver, the beloved of that old Saint's Christlike heart, stemmed the tears that coursed down his thin cheeks. He could be grateful that he had heard and answered the call. That he had gone from the presence of Alfonso to pen the letter to the Father Provincial of the society at Barcelona, begging to be sent to the missions of the New World. . . .

"For a long time, now, God has been pitifully knocking at the door of my heart and I have kept it shut until now. Reflecting that from this course my soul may be exposed to grave danger, I have decided to delay no longer but to listen and follow the voice of my Lord. . . . For the love of Jesus and the sufferings of Mary, I entreat your reverence to admit me into the number of your chosen sons, destined for the sublime ministry of the apostleship among the Gentiles. The voice of the Lord which calls me to the missions makes itself felt very strongly in my heart and stimulates me to undertake this apostleship.

"I know that I am unworthy of so great a favor, but I hope to make myself worthy, with the grace of God. . . . The desire to save souls is the only motive that inspires me."

Here and now was the desire fulfilled. Here was Pedro Claver, priest and religious of the Society of Jesus, doing the work appointed for him by the Divine Will.

Only a few moments before, a woman of wealth and fashion had left his dingy confessional in the aura of new-found holiness. The mortified son of Brother Alfonso Rodriguez thus recorded one more triumph in his holy vocation, and from heaven the once lowly lay brother looked down and rejoiced in the conquest made by the child of his heart.

Part III

The Hour of Ave Maria

Chapter I

MORE THAN three decades had passed since Doña Isabel d'Urbina had paid her first memorable visit to the chapel of the Jesuit fathers.

Lovely she was as in the days when she had come from Sevilla to Cartagena of the Indies, a joyous maiden, to be claimed by her stalwart and somber Don Pedro. Black as the shadows at nightfall over the slopes of Our Lady of La Popa was her hair, untouched by time. Still smooth was her lofty forehead and still bright and sparkling her thoughtful eyes.

Countless times had the aged bell ringer passed through the Calle de la Media Luna since Isabel had placed herself under the guidance of Father Pedro Claver. In following his wise direction she had found peace and a deeper understanding of life, with the courage and fortitude to meet and conquer its difficulties and problems.

The amazing apostolate of her Father in Christ to the poor blacks had gone on, year after year, ever seeming to increase in scope and intensity. He was loved and honored throughout all Cartagena, but most of all by his black "children," who called him their "Good Father." There would always be the few who were disposed to censure and find fault with the servant of God. Yet even these, when they spoke of him, said that he was *"muy mortifi-cado"* . . . "very mortified."

To Isabel's secret sorrow the Apostle of the Slaves had greatly altered since the days of her first meeting with him. His naturally slight figure had seemed to shrink to meager proportions and the fine fretwork of lines carved on his forehead had deepened. Father Claver appeared much older than his actual years. But Isabel and everyone else in the city knew that behind those lines which pain and privation had left, dwelled thoughts stainless as those of the blessed in Heaven.

Doña Isabel was content in the knowledge that she had contributed much to the happiness of Father Claver by her continuous outpouring of gifts for his Negroes. Her lovely fingers were frequently employed in sewing ribbons on the medals which Claver gave to the newly baptized ones; in hemming pieces of fine cloth to be used in his ministrations to the sick and in preparing baskets of good things for distribution by those faithful hands. More frequently was Liseta — long happily married to Manuel — sent by her mistress to carry mysterious bulging parcels to the little damp house in the Calle de San Ignacio. The Negress was thankful that this privilege fell to her lot — often Father Claver himself took the parcels from her; as reward, he would give her a special blessing and word of encouragement.

Isabel had finally achieved the wish she had cherished for years in secret. She had looked into the eyes of the saintly man whom God had sent to Cartagena for its salvation, as many declared. For, once the Apostle, speaking of the things of the spirit, had glanced up and looked fixedly at something in the room. . . . In earlier days she had experienced not only a pious wish to look into the eyes of a Saint, but a little of woman's curiosity to know their color.

When at last Isabel's wish was gratified, she forgot all about the color. For those eyes of a Saint seemed to be directed far beyond their immediate confines and the things of time. Their expression must have been that of the eyes of the Saviour as He stood before His tormentors, crowned with thorns and a reed in His hand.

The hill of perfection which her director had encouraged his noble penitent to climb had been steep for the dainty little feet Don Pedro had called "bewitching" in the young days of their marriage. She recalled how her noble husband had joked with her over what he called her obstinate refusal to show more of them, in the far-back days in Sevilla when, before leaving for America, he had come to stand under her balcony and serenade her.

All that seemed very remote, now. And it was very remote. Better things, even, than her stainless courtship and the ardor of wedded life had claimed Isabel. Pedro remained a steadfast soul, inclined to quiet, sometimes a little too serious, always respectful and, in his own courteous way, an adoring husband.

To some extent Isabel had overcome her repugnance to unpleasant sights and odors, yet she had never visited the slave pens. The prudent Claver refrained from asking his fine lady penitents to share his labors for the slaves, although he constantly urged them to mortification and to works of mercy and charity proper to their state.

Standing on the balcony overlooking the patio of the d'Urbina mansion, Isabel held tightly to a tiny waterpot as she cared for her flowers. She was thinking of something she had heard from the slave girl, Antonetta.

According to Antonetta, Father Claver had called at the home of her mistress to pay a visit to a Negro who was suffering from a vicious attack of ulcers. The hideous sores were distributed all over his body. They tormented him to such an extent that the unhappy man decided death would be preferable to life. From that moment he had refused to take a morsel of food.

Father Claver's eyes had filled with tears as he looked at the unhappy sufferer. After praying over him and blessing him, he finally induced the Negro to take a small particle of food. But after holding the particle in his mouth for a few moments, the slave rejected it into a dish the priest held before him.

"My child," Father Pedro then said, with great compassion, "you must not do so. Look at me!" And he had taken up the rejected morsel and swallowed it — to the utter stupefaction and chagrin of the sick man.

Heartened by the charity and self-denial of Claver, the Negro promised that he would abandon his intention of starving himself to death and would take the nourishment offered him. He kept this promise and was soon wholly cured.

So absorbed had she become in meditation that Doña Isabel forgot what she was doing. She relaxed her hold on the little waterpot and it fell into the patio. Fortunately, it escaped the head of her noble husband, who had just stepped out beside the fountain.

Don Pedro was accompanied by a guest; he beckoned to his wife to come below.

The guest was Don Diego de Villegas, and the business on which he had come could better be told to the ears of a woman than those of a man. Actually, Don Diego had come with the intention of consulting Isabel on an unfortunate family quarrel between two persons whom both knew well.

A Cartagenian lady of high rank was intent on securing a divorce from her husband because of a misunderstanding between the two. This lady had gone for advice to a high official of the place. The official had recommended her to Don Diego de Villegas and his wife. The de Villegas had tried by every means in their power to persuade the over-wrought lady to become reconciled with her husband, who was behaving just as obstinately as she.

"My wife and I have tried every means we could devise to settle this affair happily," Don Diego said. "But nothing will alter the minds of those two people. In fact, every time that either of us has talked to the wife, she has become more obdurate than before. She even threatened to hang herself sooner than return to her husband."

Isabel and Don Pedro exchanged compassionate glances. Isabel spoke first.

"If Don Diego will speak to Father Claver, I am sure he will go to visit the couple and persuade them to give up this foolish feud."

The proposition received full support from the two men. In a few minutes Don Diego had gone to find Father Claver and ask his help.

When the caller arrived the Apostle was giving a cate-chetical instruction to several hundred slaves in the patio of the college. Don Diego had heard much about Claver, but he had never up to this time witnessed him at his favorite work of teaching the poor blacks. He stood in the background, looking on rather stupidly. He felt that he was intruding on something sacred which an ordinary human being like himself was not supposed to witness.

Father Claver stood in the midst of his spiritual chil-dren. His habit hung loosely on his thin figure. His head was a little inclined in loving contemplation of his dear neophytes. His left hand rested on the shoulder of a black man, crouched at his feet — the latter evidently wished to be as close to his Good Father as possible.

With right hand uplifted, Claver was teaching the slaves to make the Sign of the Cross. With infinite patience he repeated his instruction again and again, employing the simplest words of explanation. Occasionally he would ask those who were apparently his brightest pupils to repeat the sacred act after him. If they were successful they were rewarded with a glorious smile.

When any slight reproof issued from the lips of the Apostle to two or three Negroes, who appeared somewhat disinterested in the proceedings, it was given very gently. Father Claver never scolded or intimidated anyone.

Most of his flock were seated on the ground. A few, the older and more infirm slaves, occupied places on rude blocks of stone or boxes their Good Father had set in place to serve as seats.

The priest remained standing during the entire instruction. After a time he leaned against the trunk of a palm tree, but that was all. The cloak, so frequently utilized as a coverlet for the leprous and ulcerous blacks, was wrapped carefully about the emaciated body of an aged Negro. . . .

These slaves had been but a short time in Cartagena. They had arrived in the latest shipment from the Congo and Angola and from the coasts of Guinea. Their faces registered varying degrees of intelligence, but the majority of them looked up into the face of their Father in God with an expression of admiration, gratitude, and awe.

Don Diego de Villegas watched the striking scene with bewilderment and a sense of personal shame. In the presence of such Christlike charity and self-denial the man of the world saw his own littleness as in a mirror that has power to distort the figure presented before it.

Claver's face was pale and worn, yet radiant with contentment as he noted the ready response to his efforts. . . . Don Diego recalled the titles by which the Apostle was known throughout Cartagena. Yes; this frail, angelic priest was in very truth the Good Father of the Negroes; the Saint of the tradesmen and laborers, and the Angel of Peace of the noble citizens of Cartagena.

At the close of his exhortation, Claver led the slaves in

their prayer, making them repeat after him in their own language these invocations:

"Jesus Christ, only-begotten Son of God, Thou art our Father, our Treasure, all our Good. We love Thee with all our hearts. We are sincerely sorry for having offended Thee. Lord, we promise never again to leave Thee. Our strength, our souls, our bodies, all that we have we consecrate to Thee, forever, unto eternity. We love Thee above all things; we adore Thee; we prefer Thee to our own life. Permit us not to fall into sin. Send us death in preference! It will be more satisfying for us to die than to live in enmity with Thee."

The tired voice of the priest trailed off a little at the end, although he repeated a part of the prayer again and again, syllable by syllable, that it might become firmly rooted in the guileless and untrained minds of his hearers.

"Jesus Christ . . . we love Thee . . . with all our hearts . . . We prefer Thee. . . . Permit us not . . . fall into sin . . . death . . . in preference. . . ."

Don Diego de Villegas stood apart, eyes downcast, a little embarrassed as the Negroes filed out of the patio. But first they crowded about the priest, some venerating his tired hands, others his feet — and at this he appeared distressed, for with the withdrawing of the hem of his habit the torn alpargates were revealed, together with the cords binding his toes.

Tired the Apostle was, yes, for the day had been crowded with duties and trials. Most trying of all, he had read in the faces of one or two of those to whom he was bound by ties of fraternal charity a furtive look of disapproval. He humbly accepted the cross. They did not understand. But the realization cast a shadow on the sensitive heart that sought nothing for itself, deeming itself worthy only of the worst and others worthy of all the best things life had to bestow.

Father Claver knew Don Diego de Villegas very well, for the latter had frequently aided him to obtain favors for his persecuted blacks. He approached the nobleman and, greeting him cordially, bade him follow him into the house.

In the parlor Diego seated himself, at Father Claver's invitation. To put his visitor more at ease the priest himself sat down on the very edge of a chair.

Diego at once made known his errand. Claver was gravely concerned. Because of the position which the divided couple occupied, a scandal would result if the quarrel were to become public matter. And, a thing far more consequential in the Apostle's eye was the offense to God should this husband and wife ruthlessly break the sacred bond which united them in holy matrimony.

Father Claver promised to go at once to visit the couple and see what could be done to make peace between them.

His first attempt did not appear to be successful. He tried to reason with husband and wife, but both remained inflexible, assuring him that they were determined to carry out their plan of separation.

Urged to do so by his wife and Doña Isabel d'Urbina, the kindhearted Diego himself called on the pair. But scarcely had he entered the house when he heard frightful screams, coming from one of the rooms upstairs.

Rushing up, he found the mistress of the house pale and terrified. Questioning her, he learned that she had been taking a siesta when, in her dream, two devils suddenly appeared before her — one at either side of her bed. They threatened to do her bodily harm and not only her but likewise the attorneys who had undertaken to defend her cause.

Again Diego went in search of Father Claver. And again the Apostle visited the unhappy woman. This time her husband was present. This time both listened to the words of warning and counsel addressed to them.

Meanwhile, Don Diego had waited outside the house. When Father Claver appeared and told him that on the following Monday — two days later — the trouble would be satisfactorily adjusted, he rejoiced. Diego afterward heard from the reconciled couple that they were unable to resist Father Claver's powerful plea.

Doña Isabel d'Urbina also rejoiced when she heard of the happy outcome of the visit. She believed that the consolations granted to her saintly director must be overwhelming since he was able to bring such great peace and healing to troubled and storm-tossed hearts.

Isabel would have been deeply edified could she have looked in on her revered Father later that day as he ministered to the sick Negroes.

Among the slaves belonging to Don Manuel Acosta, a wealthy planter, a contagious disease had broken out. Soon its victims were a mass of putrid sores. When Father Claver heard of this he went to visit the sufferers, who were isolated in an outhouse on their master's estate.

However strong in virtue and practiced in the art of overcoming nature he was, the heroic priest almost fainted when he saw the miserable condition of the Negroes. It seemed that he must leave the infected place at once and go into the fresh air.

Sternly reproving himself for what he deemed his cowardice and inhumanity, he went aside, where the Negroes could not see him. Taking a discipline from his pocket he administered a severe punishment to the poor body he believed had betrayed him.

After that he went courageously to the side of the plague-stricken blacks and ministered to souls and bodies alike.

It was Father Claver's way of dealing with that lower

nature which he judged had so nearly betrayed its master, the unconquerable spirit of a priest of the Most High. It was as if he had said:

"A great thing it is that this donkey of mine should want to practice one of his tricks . . . to show that he is still alive! Now we shall see if he can have his own way!"

Chapter II

AT THE CLOSE of the long afternoon siesta, taken during the hottest hours of day, the shopkeepers of Cartagena had thrown back the shutters of their establishments and were preparing to take advantage of whatsoever business might be abroad.

Diego Gomez was one of the fortunate ones on whom Providence had ,bestowed a goodly share of material treasure. On his shelves rested bales of the finest silks, velvets, and linens, with the meaner cloth stuffs which sufficed for the poor folk. The cloth market had been brisk of late and the merchant rubbed his hands in gleeful anticipation of the additional pesos that would soon ring in his coffers.

Diego looked down the street to a mauve-colored house having unusually fine iron grilles across the windows. A richly caparisoned gallant had tethered his horse to the gate, and, with plumed hat sweeping the sand at his feet, was saluting the lady of his heart. She, poor thing, was to be pitied, Diego told himself. For, albeit her point of vantage was sufficient to enable her to see her swain, the distance that separated them rendered the meeting somewhat painful.

Diego knew the house well. The young person on the balcony, whose charming form was all too adequately protected by a straw matting that ran around all sides, was a relative of its noble mistress. Only heaven knew where she had met the young man, who now craned his neck higher, in order better to glimpse the little of his lady there was to be seen.

The shopkeeper chuckled and wagged his head from side to side as he pondered the long and rather melancholy courtship that must ensue before the desolated youth might claim the girl as his bride.

There would be tedious evenings, when he must sit in the family circle, with his beloved as far removed from him as the length of the room would permit, and listen to conversation that would prove exceedingly dull to an impetuous lover. He would be obliged to lend an ear, with an air of exceeding interest, to the recital by some old grandee of Segovia or Cadiz, of the journey made by Don Pedro de Heredia from Santo Domingo to Cartagena of the Indies. . . . Old men generally lived in the past and so it would be with the courtly forebears of Doña Ana's young relative. It would hardly be prudent for the suitor to indulge in a yawn as the tale progressed; to do so would be to discourage future visits to the house. He must lend an attentive soul to descriptions of the articulated leather breastplates which experienced captains had advised Heredia to wear as protection against the poisoned arrows of the Indians, or of that doughty general's lancing and disemboweling of the savages. The details of the latter might well cause the ladies to turn pale and hide their faces behind their fans.

Another consideration was still more unsatisfactory. When the young lover wished to take his lady to the Dialogues, the whole family must accompany the couple. From an economic viewpoint, even if from none other, this was not desirable.

Just then the cloth merchant suffered a distraction.

A light thud resounded outside his door. Diego grew pale and disturbed; he glanced toward his blessed shelves in a fever of well-justified apprehension.

The light thud proceeded from the walking stick, surmounted by a cross, which Father Pedro Claver often carried, with one of his inevitable satchels for alms slung upon it.

"God bless this house and those who dwell in it!" the priest said. "I come to beg a little present for my lepers. The poor fellows are without mosquito bars and the insects leave them no peace. We have to take care of that. Any little piece of cloth suited to the purpose will be a rich present to me and my children in Jesus Christ. Heaven will abundantly reward the charity."

Father Pedro was thinking that he would enlist the services of two Negresses, on whom he could rely, to cut the cloth into mosquito bars.

The shopkeeper bent awkwardly, for he was portly to the extent of being all creases, like a great pig, to receive the blessing of the priest.

It seemed incredible that Father Pedro could endure so many self-inflicted miseries and yet live to trudge about the streets as merrily as if he were a small boy in pursuit of the barquillero, vendor of sweet cakes, a peseto or two tucked snugly in his small fist. The merchant recalled that he had never seen the priest act as if he minded the heat or humidity, although tiny rivulets of moisture were even now settled in the ridges on his forehead. Nor did he ever allude to the sting of the insect bites that invariably decorated his hands and face.

Far be it from Diego to understand such an unaccountable manner of life or such a unique philosophy as that in the life of Pedro Claver.

He waited in trepidation for the priest to indicate how much of the cloth he expected to receive.

But Father Claver said nothing about that. He had stated his case and now he waited for the response.

Waddling to that part of the shop where the cloth was kept, the shopkeeper unrolled a very little of it. Out of the corner of his eye he watched the face of his tormentor; as yet it registered no emotion of satisfaction whatsoever. Diego's stinginess could hardly be pleasing to the generous-souled Apostle.

When several yards had been unrolled on the counter and its owner had estimated his loss, there was still no indication that the amount was sufficient. Father Claver was regarding the material intently and interestedly, while beneath his breath the merchant was muttering certain somethings — he was not saying his prayers.

Finally, under the pressure of Claver's reproachful eyes, the holocaust was consummated. The entire roll of white stuff slid into the satchel.

The cloth merchant bethought himself of something he believed would be certain to increase his prestige in the eyes of the Apostle. He had a piece of gossip to divulge; it should serve as *"el broche de oro,"* the golden hook, wherewith to attach himself more securely to the good will and prayers of Father Claver.

It appeared that the father of a youth named Emmanuel Rodriguez had become involved in numerous difficulties, due to the evil propensities of his son. By paying considerable sums of money to injured parties the distressed parent had kept the matter from public knowledge. Such a state of affairs could not continue indefinitely, else the nobleman would soon find himself a poor man. And when there were no more moneys to pay — what?

Diego vouchsafed it as his private opinion that the elegant but vicious youth, Emmanuel, would be choked to death some fine morning in the Plaza, while the honest folks of Cartagena looked admiringly on — a spike at the

STREET OF THE HALF-MOON 161

back of a hempen collar would do the job neatly, the shopkeeper opined.

Father Claver did not thank his informant profusely, or, indeed, at all for the information. He appeared to ignore it. With an expression of gratitude for the cloth and a blessing for the fat little Diego, he departed. The serenity of his countenance was a little obscured by a look of anxiety the shopkeeper did not notice. The Apostle keenly felt any insult offered to his Blessed Lord, any loss to souls, consequent on sin. According to what he had just heard, a certain youth in Cartagena was doing much to drive the thorns deeper into the wounded brow of the Saviour.

After he had performed his penitential practices that evening Father Claver threw himself on the high mat and fell into a light slumber. This slumber, however, was shortly broken by an imperious summons of the doorbell.

Instantly he was up and descending the stairs — this he did so speedily that the portero had no need to call him.

As Father Claver had surmised, the call was to the bedside of the sick.

In a few minutes he was hurrying down the narrow street before the college, turning into the Calle de Santa Teresa, thence into Santo Domingo, a street of fine mansions.

His visit was to the home of an exemplary Christian, Don Augustin de Barona, one of the witnesses at the garrotting of the Spanish captain whom Claver had attended in his last hour.

When the priest entered the sick chamber he found Don Augustin propped up on the lace-covered pillows in a great canopied bed. His eyes were burning with fever and his body was inert and nerveless. Barona had been ill for some time, but no one in the household had realized the seriousness of his condition.

The sick man's wife and son waited outside the door of

the chamber while Father Claver and Barona conversed for an hour and a half. At the end of that time the young man became anxious, also a little curious to know what was going on. He opened the door a few inches.

The Apostle was on his knees beside the bed. With his hands clasped, he was beseeching the sick man to recommend him to God, when, "on the morrow," Barona should enter the Divine Presence!

Barona's wife and son were overwhelmed with grief at Father Claver's words. The attending physician had told them that the patient was progressing favorably. . . . And now the good and kind husband and father was to go from his dear ones — on the morrow!

The grief-stricken couple continued to watch and listen, for the time of intimate spiritual revelation had passed.

They saw the dying man lift himself and embrace his Spiritual Father. They heard him promise the priest that he would be sure to remember him before God, as he had requested.

When Father Claver came from the room he found Barona's wife and son weeping freely. The boy was trying to comfort his mother by reminding her of something that had not penetrated her distraught mind.

"But Father Pedro said that our dear one will be with God as soon as he leaves this earth. In heaven he will watch over us and help us!"

The priest spoke reassuringly to the two, then bade them return to the bedside of the dying and recite some prayers.

The night was very dark. As Father Claver left the house he walked slowly, for he was weary and, also, he wished to recite his rosary for his friend.

A light flurry of raindrops, lasting for about five minutes, soaked through his thin garments, although a few minutes later the earth appeared quite dry, as usual in the tropics. He could hear the low swell of the Caribbean, moaning beyond its huge granite barrier, as if that massive barricade of Philip II were a "wailing wall." The thick leaves of the uva tree with the clusters of sour grapes peeping from between moved restlessly in the night wind. . . . Through openings between the houses and trees the priest saw the shimmering waters, ribbed like rock crystal and restless as troubled thoughts.

The heavy creepers wormed their way about the tree trunks like sinister serpents, writhing at every stir of the breeze. All nature seemed attuned to a somber symphony tonight.

Father Claver quickened his steps as a shadow passed across the clear surface of his soul.

The blackness had now become so dense that it was not possible to see beyond two or three paces. He had nearly run against a huge papuan tree, whose thick roots spread out over the sandy path, before he saw it.

A moment later he stood still beside the tree that had assumed a more hideous appearance as he approached.

In a voice trembling with horror and displeasure, he cried out:

"Beware, miserable man! Death is on the watch behind that tree!"

Swift as the descent of the rain a few moments before, a dark figure glided from its hiding place behind the giant tree trunk and slunk away into the blackness.

The warning of Father Claver had struck with the terrific force of a bolt of lightning into the soul of young Emmanuel Rodriguez. With evil intent he had placed himself behind the tree, waiting for an opportunity to carry it out.

Father Claver had not seen the youth, for in the rear section of the trunk there was a wide deep cavity, capable of hiding the body of a man.

Emmanuel's father never knew what had occasioned the sudden and providential change in the behavior of his son. Nor did the shopkeeper, Diego Gomez.

Only two beside Emmanuel knew — God and Father Claver.

So the papuan tree with its distorted branches and its gaunt creepers was the occasion of another triumph for the Apostle of Cartagena, who on many a torrid afternoon had taught a group of Negroes in its shade.

Chapter III

A HEAVY DOWNPOUR of tropical rain had converted the radiant old city of Don Pedro de Heredia into a veritable sea of mud. Deserted was the Great Market, El Mercado, close to the harbor, behind which the twin towers of San Ignacio rose like sentinels. The Government Palace and the cathedral resembled huge gray clouds on the horizon and the green cross on La Inquisición gleamed like a sinister jewel whose price was misfortune to all who came under its baleful influence. Little rivulets descended from the upper galleries of the magnificent old palaces, to widen the ever-increasing pools on the pavements. Under the banana and palm, the bonga and ceiba trees, scores of little black children danced for joy, holding up their hands to catch the drops shaken from the thickly clustered leaves. Beyond the shadowy arch in the Baluarte de San Antonio, at the end of the Calle de la Media Luna, the Caribbean struggled as if with mighty passions, while, far up on its austere heights, Santa Cruz de La Popa, Our Lady's Monastery of the Holy Cross, strained like a huge galleon breasting the turbulent and lowering ocean wastes.

Accompanied by Brother Gonzalez, Father Pedro Claver strode through the unpleasant streets as if he was unaware that the rain was descending in torrents. He walked so quickly that the brother, who found it a hard task to keep

up with him, was scolding a little. If the Apostle heard what
he said, he gave no indication of it.

Brother Gonzalez was saying that if Claver were to contract a heavy cold — as it seemed he must do, since he had
been running about since early morning — his work for
the slaves would necessarily suffer.

Brother never attempted to lecture any of the other
members of his Community in that fashion, nor did he
find it necessary. Only one Jesuit in Cartagena of the
Indies insisted upon doing what only a donkey could do
and escape unharmed.

That thought brought a distraction to the good brother
as he remembered that the priest always spoke of himself
as a beast of burden, fit only to bear the weight of his
own shortcomings and those of his black children in Christ.
To Father Pedro's companion it all seemed very much out
of order, and he could not approve it.

At last it seemed that Claver had finished his work for
that day. But Brother Gonzalez reckoned badly. For he
was to wait, standing in the pouring rain, outside a certain
house in the Calle de Santo Domingo, while the Apostle
accomplished an errand of spiritual mercy for a young
negro girl.

The house was the residence of a Spanish lady prominent in the social life of the city. As the two religious
approached it, Father Claver slackened his pace, then
stopped.

At the door of the mansion a young slave girl was
seated, busily sewing. The Apostle walked toward her and
asked whether her mistress was at home.

The slave arose and curtsied reverently.

"Yes, Good Father," she replied. "My little mistress is
at home. I am sure she would be pleased to have Your
Reverence come in."

To brother's surprise, Father Claver went in; he did not

usually enter any of the fine houses unless to visit the sick.

Brother could not know what went on inside, but he was very curious concerning it. . . .

In the sittingroom Father Claver waited, standing, while the young Negress went to call her mistress.

The latter soon appeared, wondering what could be the reason for the unusual visit.

Father Pedro came to the point at once.

"Señora," he said, "you must send that young slave girl to confession this very day."

The noble lady was still more astonished to hear this. When she had sufficiently recovered her composure to reply, she asked:

"Father, why such haste? She is perfectly well."

Claver spoke in a calm confident tone:

"Never mind. Send her to confession, for the day will not come to its end without some misfortune befalling her. Be sure to see that she receives the sacraments. If you do not, you will repent of it."

Stern and uncompromising as the words seemed, they were spoken in a mild and compassionate tone.

The mistress of the slave could not be offended, although she was accustomed to issue rather than receive commands.

She promised the Apostle that she would send the girl to the church and see that she made her confession as soon as possible.

Brother Gonzalez was very glad when he saw Father Claver coming out of the house.

"We must return at once, Father," Brother ventured. "It is almost time for the Community exercises."

He noticed that the priest appeared unusually weary and that he sighed heavily, as if he was oppressed. Once he took from his habit a piece of old cloth and wiped the moisture from his forehead and eyes, in order to see the path ahead.

The practical brother grunted disapprovingly at this exhibition of poverty. He knew that every article of the kind given Father Claver for his personal use was handed to the slaves. Claver would start out in the morning with a supply of white handkerchiefs, some of which Doña Isabel d'Urbina had certainly worked with her dainty hands. The handkerchiefs would be placed in his pocket by Brother Gonzalez himself, who always received them when Doña Isabel sent the precious packages to the college. That noble lady was aware that her holy director would not notice the fine stitches on the linen, but she had the satisfaction of knowing that for a brief time it would rest close to the heart that was the cradle of so many tormented human creatures.

The mist was thick before the eyes of the two men as they proceeded, at a slower pace. The Apostle of the Slaves was plainly exhausted. Yet he was amazingly cheerful. Looking from the corner of his eye, brother noted that Claver's face wore a faraway look. He would not have addressed a word to him just then, for anything in the world. He knew that he was holding intimate communion with his Maker and deriving new courage from the thought of the graces showered upon him in the past and the wonderful opportunities opened to him in this apostleship to the slaves, so filled with loneliness and suffering yet so amazingly fruitful.

Thinking now of the reproaches he had sometimes heard heaped on the head of the saintly man at his side by those who misjudged him because they were less pure than he, Brother Gonzalez wondered whether in moments of such weariness as he was now experiencing, Father Pedro ever became aware of the human part of him. Of the longings of a normal man for the innocent gratification of his senses; for the comfort of a soft bed and the legitimate satisfactions allowed to a body more sensitive than that of most men; for the touch of a loving mother's hands instead of hands running with vile ulcers or hardened as an old board by rude incessant labor in the mines or on the plantations.

Brother Gonzalez sighed in turn — and gave up the problem of Father Claver. No man could know what went on in the heart of a saint unless that saint chose to reveal it. And, as every religious in the little Community at San Ignacio knew well, Father Pedro could never be brought to say anything at all about himself unless to reiterate that he was a worthless beast of burden and that he wondered how the good Lord had the patience to bear with his many infirmities.

Brother thought of the young slave girl back in the Calle de Santo Domingo . . . a girl, sewing on a bit of fine cloth. He wondered what the priest had noticed about her that had caused him to go so quickly into the house of her mistress.

But at this point he was speedily recalled from his reverie by the voice of his companion. Claver, as if he himself were the inferior in rank and Brother his superior, quietly begged him:

"Be patient for a little while, Brother . . . it is a matter of helping a soul. Come with me!"

Brother Gonzalez could never grow accustomed to these unforeseen and unexpected alterations in Father Claver's program. Yet on the present occasion he forebore to grumble that the towers of San Ignacio were already in sight and that the pair were expected home at that very moment.

Following closely on the heels of the Apostle, Brother soon found himself in a section of the city called Getsemani. Claver at once sought a certain street and hurried along it until he reached a small and very miserable hut. This he entered at once, without knocking.

Stretched prone on a mat in a corner a poor Indian lay

in the agony of death. Happily he was still conscious. When he saw the face of the priest bending over him, he smiled feebly and muttered something. His fingers sought his neck — there was the medal given him by Father Claver, for the dying Indian was a baptized Christian.

Brother Gonzalez retired, as gracefully as he could, into the rain, while Father Claver did what he had to do.

He first heard the Indian's confession, then, having admitted his companion, administered the other sacraments. After that he remained by the bedside of the dying man until the latter peacefully expired upon his spiritual Father's breast.

Brother was smitten with remorse for the impatience he had shown during the afternoon. . . . He could think of no other explanation of the unexpected visit of Father Pedro to the hut than that God had made known to him the needs of a dying man.

To the brother's infinite relief the two reached the College of the Jesuit Fathers shortly after. Father Claver was most solicitous about the drenched condition of his companion; he urged Gonzalez to go to his room at once, remove his wet garments and adopt measures against contracting a cold.

"But, Father, what of yourself?" Brother asked, seeing that the priest was taking no thought of his own condition.

Claver settled that matter instantly.

"My donkey is not worth thinking about!" he replied.

Brother lost no time in ridding himself of his wet clothing and taking a strong dose of preventive medicine. Then he settled down to his night prayers.

Tonight they were a trifle distracted. Despite all he could do to prevent, a scene persisted in returning to his inner vision. A dried-up old Indian, a dirty specimen, stretched on a wretched bed, scarcely fit for an animal.

. . . Yet Father Claver had leaned on that bed as he lovingly ministered to the stricken man. Brother himself had fought a winning battle to keep from holding his hand to his nose, which was violently assaulted by the distressing odors proceeding from both bed and occupant. Father Pedro had appeared not to notice them. While Brother Gonzalez conceded full credit to the heroic missionary, he felt certain that God had endowed him with very special graces, enabling him to go on without wavering in his self-sacrificing apostolate.

Brother had forgotten the young slave girl whom the priest had intercepted at the door of her mistress's house. The following day, toward evening, as he passed along the Calle de Santo Domingo, he was startled to see a funeral cortege leaving the mansion. He was told that a young slave of the household had suddenly expired on the previous evening.

Returning from an errand, she was in very high spirits, they said. She had accompanied her mistress to the church and received the sacraments. As she entered the door of the house, a little song was on her lips. Suddenly, however, the melody died away in a cry of pain. The slave girl fell to the floor, unconscious. Various remedies were applied, but in vain. Nothing served to arouse her. In a few hours she had died.

Brother Gonzalez was lacking neither in intelligence nor in spirituality. At once he linked the extraordinary visit of Father Claver to the house on the previous evening with this sudden death.

As soon as he reached the college, he lost no time in acquainting the Father Superior with his experience.

The superior made no comment. He could rely on Brother Gonzalez to be discreet. He was becoming accustomed to receiving these reports of extraordinary happenings in connection with Claver's mission.

Upstairs, in his room, the humble subject of this interest was busy at work, writing on a great many slips of paper certain teachings of the Catholic Faith. These slips of paper were for his black neophytes. His hands were so tired that often the pen dropped from his fingers. Again and again he forced himself to go on with his task. When the drowsiness persisted, he abruptly laid down the work. . . .

Always, when he found his "donkey" obdurate he knew what to do to bring him into subjection to the spirit.

He did that thing now.

When he had finished, his flesh was so sorely wounded by the merciless strokes of the lash that he was very wide awake.

Chapter IV

TO A LITTLE COTTAGE in the country, a short distance from Cartagena, Don Pedro d'Urbina had been removed, by his wife's order, that he might breathe purer air in the illness that was rapidly reducing his strength. Don Pedro was suffering from an infectious disease that had invaded Cartagena and its suburbs. Every means had been tried in the effort to restore him to health. None had proved effective.

Doña Isabel studied the wan but still handsome countenance of her husband as he lay propped up on lace-covered pillows. Manuel, Don Pedro's groom, now a gray-haired Negro, sat beside him, wielding a fan rather too listlessly to bring any relief to the invalid.

To Jeromina, Isabel confided her fears.

"He is failing rapidly. I have only one resource left. If Father Claver were to come here and pray over him, surely he would get well."

Jeromina nodded her head in assent; the same thought had been in her mind.

Isabel at once dispatched a slave to the church of the Jesuit Fathers at Cartagena with an urgent plea that the Apostle come as soon as possible to Don Pedro's side.

When she had watched the messenger disappearing down the country road she wandered into the luxuriant gardens at the rear of the estate. In a small shed near by Manuel, now released from sickroom duty, was grooming César, her husband's favorite mount, after another slave had brought him in from a stiff ride.

Isabel's eyes rested on the noble beast which, in turn, regarded her with something of a quizzical expression in its dark eyes.

Where, César seemed to ask, was his brave and debonair master? Where was Don Pedro d'Urbina on such a fine afternoon, when the air was cool and fragrant after the tropical shower and the smell of damp earth steamed up invitingly?

Isabel stroked the nose of the beautiful animal. A mist gathered before her eyes, eyes that showed fine lines about them, after days and nights of anxious vigil.

César seemed to continue his questioning of his mistress by the movements of his graceful head and his covert glances from side to side.

Should not Don Pedro be even now in the saddle, his velour hat pulled low over his forehead to shield his eyes from the glare of sun and sand, his firm hands resting idly on the bridle as he followed the trail that led into the wood? Through those woods, long before, César's valiant namesake had journeyed in search of new territory for his master, Don Pedro de Heredia, lieutenant of Philip II. Francesco de César was an honored name in Cartagena of the Indies, for he who bore it had been a man of honor and sacrifice.

Por supuesto! . . . Of course! . . . Don Pedro d'Urbina would soon appear! Meanwhile, César would do his best to remind Isabel of his special liking for panela cakes. When the cakes had been consumed, delicious morsels over which César was wont to linger as long as possible, master and horse would set forth. Cuban palms, imported into New Granada, would then move by like columns of

Indians in retreat, and red monkeys, chattering their indistinguishable jargon, would throw nuts on the head of Don Pedro as he rode beneath the low-hanging branches of the casuarina and mango trees.

Perhaps this time the noble master would be inclined to turn down by the water, where he could look out over the ever-moving, ever-turbulent aquamarine waves. . . . In any event, he would come out soon!

Isabel, her head and shoulders wrapped about in a gauze veil as protection against the insects that abounded where the verdure was so thick, stood with her firmly moulded figure pressed against César's flank, as if she would derive comfort from the thing that had been near and dear to Don Pedro. She had already commissioned Manuel to go for more panela cakes.

The far-off, bell-like note of the campañero sounded in the quiet spot. The bird was probably some half mile distant, flitting in and out among the ceibas and palms. Butterflies darted about on all sides; in the tropics, because of their great number, they were almost a pest.

Manuel now approached with the panela, done up in a banana leaf.

Isabel fed the sweet cakes to César in morsels, so as to prolong his enjoyment of them. Listlessly, then, she watched the little caravans of burros, loaded with well-filled sacks, winding over the sandy road beyond the cottage. When the last of them had passed from sight she gathered her wide skirts about her and went into the house.

In his chamber Don Pedro was lying very still, his great dark eyes staring straight ahead as if he saw far beyond the confines of the room.

"I have sent for Father Claver," Isabel said, simply, seating herself on the bed.

The sick man smiled and touched the medal of Nuestra Señora he always wore about his neck. Then, with his wife's hand tucked securely within his own, he fell into a light slumber.

Left alone once more, Isabel's thoughts centered on the stern realization which every human being must one day face, the inevitable parting with a beloved one.

Parting. . . . Yet, surely, Don Pedro would recover from this illness. Father Claver would see to that, for the Apostle was a favored servant of God, who had wrought many wonderful things in Cartagena. He would soon be there! The assurance brought comfort and a sense of security to Isabel's oppressed heart.

Looking intently at the silver crucifix on her husband's breast, she bowed her head and prayed. Not in the ordinary prayers of the Church or in petitions suggested by her own great need and that of her loved one. But, rather, in the poesy of the mystical Teresa, called "of Jesus," — her countrywoman, who also had suffered. . . .

> "*Innocente Cordero,*
>   *En tu sangre banado,*
>   *Con que del mundo los pecados quitas,*
>   *Del robusto madero*
>   *Por los brazas colgado,*
>   *Abiertos, que abrazarte a mi me incitas. . . ."*

> "Innocent Lamb,
>   Bathed in Thy Blood,
>   By which Thou hast freed the world from sin;
>   Bound on the heavy wooden beam
>   By Thy arms, opened to invite me. . . ."

The Innocent Lamb of God had been bound with cords as was the holy servant of His who would soon come to prepare the soul of Don Pedro d'Urbina for heaven. Often had Isabel sought to catch a glimpse of the feet that were made to bear the punishment of the aberrations of so many poor unfortunates and so many who were not poor in the sense that they had little education or material advantages. In the proud old city of the conquistadors, Pedro Claver had elected to live and work among the most abandoned. They had nothing to offer him in return save a boundless trust and affection and obedience to his slightest commands.

Teresa, called "of Jesus," had been made of such fiber. And there were many others. But it was Teresa, flower and glory of Old Castile, who most powerfully attracted her noble countrywoman, Isabel d'Urbina. The great Carmelite had been canonized the year Father Claver made his solemn profession in the Society of San Ignacio de Loyola. Teresa de Cepeda y Ahumada, crimson flower of divine love, had provided her people with marvelous inspiration in the mystical poems which told of the fevered longings of her ardent soul for union with its Beloved.

Isabel's lips now formed the syllables of that passionate cry of yearning that best revealed the desire of Teresa:

> *"Aquesta divina union*
> *Del amor con que yo vivo,*
> *Haze a Dios ser mi cativo,*
> *Y libre mi corazon;*
> *Mas causa en mi tal pasion*
> *Ver a Dios mi prisonero*
> *Que muero porque no muero. . . ."*

> "This divine union
> Of love in which I live
> Binds my being captive to God
> And frees my heart;
> But causes in me such yearning
> Toward God, who captivates me,
> That I die because I do not die."

Isabel clasped her hands in sudden fear and anguish, as she prayed to God to spare her beloved longer to her; much longer, or a little longer if it might not be more!

Toward evening Father Claver arrived at the cottage. With him he brought the Eucharistic Saviour and the holy oils for the anointing.

After he had heard the sick man's confession and administered the last sacraments he gave him a little picture of Brother Alfonso Rodriguez.

Don Pedro's eyes took on an expression of satisfaction and confidence as he looked into the face of the priest. He pressed the likeness of Brother Alfonso to his heart as he said:

"Father, if your friend, the Saint, restores my health, I promise to give a substantial sum toward defraying the expenses of his canonization."

Father Claver prayed a long time, on his knees, entreating God to cure his noble friend if such was His Holy Will. He then departed, with a word of encouragement and counsel to both husband and wife.

Don Pedro dozed a little, while Isabel continued her prayers. When he awoke his wife was kneeling in the spot where Father Claver had knelt. To her delight, the nobleman was unusually talkative. Previously he had been silent and a little depressed.

His thoughts traveled to his loved Cartagena of the Indies. He spoke of the musical call of the church bells and how, in the late afternoon, the breeze sprang up, seemingly from nowhere. Then meadows and woods and lanes and even the sea were mantled in a mist of heliotrope. Romance, adventure, mystery seemed to lurk in every stone and leaf and ripple. Beautiful Cartagena, beautiful Queen of the Caribes!

A few moments after, Don Pedro fancied he was walking near a section of the Great Wall on which the slaves were busily working. He was speaking with a sentinel who had popped his head out of the door of his little stone box to pass the time of day with him. He inquired of the man how the work was progressing in the northeast part of the city, where the wall of Santo Domingo was in process of construction. It was this section that gave most trouble to the engineers and where the most time must of necessity be spent.

Now the sick man pointed across the room, asking Isabel to notice the bright red creepers that wound over the stones; he had always loved their brilliance; he called them La Bellissima. In a sudden fever of pain his wife realized that his mind wandered.

But in a moment, he was back in his bed, in the little cottage in the country — holding something in his thin hands.

What was it?

Ah! A dim picture. A very dim picture. Whose?

The dying man could not seem to see the picture. By a gesture he made known to Isabel that he would very much like to know whose it was.

Isabel's bright head drooped to the lace-edged bed quilt while her tears fell upon it.

The picture . . .

It was a likeness of good Brother Alfonso Rodriguez, the holy man whose intercession made sick people well.

Don Pedro brightened and tried to raise himself in order to see Alfonso better. The room was growing so dark he thought a storm must be coming on.

A moment later he fell back into the outstretched arms of Isabel. His lips moved, as he repeated the names:

"Jesu! Maria!" — "Alfonso!"

That was all. There would never be any more. The gallant and white-souled scion of a noble house in old Sevilla would never again sit astride César and, with a gay wave of the hand to his adored wife, gallop off down the road with that delicious abandon that so well became him who was in reality a rather serious man. The searching eyes of the beautiful beast which had shared so many adventures with his stout-hearted master would look wistfully this way and that. But Don Pedro would never again come for him.

Manuel would stand close and hold the bridle for others to mount; for Doña Isabel herself, or for the lady Jeromina or for one of the young nephews of the family. But the gifted and kindly master would never ride again.

Summoned by the bereaved Isabel, Father Claver returned to the cottage as quickly as possible. Isabel was worn by her long vigils and the pain of her loss; she scarcely knew what she said. Seeming to blame her Spiritual Father for failing to save her husband, she cried:

"Father, I asked you to cure him, and you let him die!"

The mortified Claver knew how to accept reproaches. This one, he realized, was not intended. But that did not matter. All that mattered was the safety of the soul of the beloved dead; that he might rest in peace in Christ and that those who mourned his passing might take heart in the thought that he was now with God.

Very gently Claver said to Isabel:

"God willed it so, my daughter. It is necessary to submit to His Holy Will."

Like a frightened wayward child, Isabel was not yet prepared to submit. She replied:

"But if you had wished it, Father, my husband would be still living. If you had asked God to cure him, he would have been spared. You did not ask for that favor; you deceived me, completely. Tell me so, plainly. Is it not true that you deceived me?"

Father Claver soothed and comforted the distraught Isabel, whose nerves had given way. He believed himself worthy of all reproaches, although in this instance he knew also that he was blameless.

He responded in the same fatherly, affectionate tone.

"No, my daughter. Do not think that. Brother Alfonso, also, earnestly begged our Lord to cure Don Pedro. But the Divine Saviour answered him: 'It is to his advantage to die now; he will never be better disposed than now.' Console yourself! Your husband is in heaven. From there he is watching over you and protecting you. You have now one more advocate to defend you. Trust in God, and continue striving to be more virtuous, my daughter."

Even as the mist of heat lifted from fields and woods when the trade wind crept in at evening, so did the veil of anguish and distrust move away from the soul of Isabel d'Urbina.

She placed implicit faith in the words of her faithful guide. She was assured that her husband was at peace with God. His generous deeds, his virtuous life, his great charities in behalf of the poor slaves had merited for him this great reward!

This — and, Isabel felt secure in believing — the united pleas of two great servants of God, Brother Alfonso Rodriguez and Father Pedro Claver.

Chapter V

AT MIDDAY the old city of Don Pedro de Heredia dozed behind its partly finished walls. The gigantic engineering project, begun in 1594 by order of Philip II, was progressing most favorably. One hundred and thirty years would have passed when, in 1717, in the rule of Don Carlos de Sucre, sixty-eighth governor of Cartagena, the last block would be set in place. This vast undertaking was to cost the treasury of Spain fifty-nine million pesos. The walls, so dear to Philip's heart, were begun sixteen years before the coming of the young religious, Pedro Claver, to the Indies.

Now, about the middle of the seventeenth century, a great part of the work had been completed. The walls were divided into two sections. The first surrounded that part of the city known as *Chambacu y Getsemani*, extending one thousand and thirty meters. Several forts were constructed in this location, notably Revellin, which afforded a strategic point of defense for the city from inland as well as from the sea. The second and more important section of the walls surrounded Cartagena on all its sides, extending three thousand and six hundred meters, the exact perimeter of the city. This section demonstrated the most remarkable and astonishing feats of military engineering. Señor Elias de Baloco, whose name one of the streets of Cartagena bore and under whose direction the work was begun, had in his day also held the posts of commander and physician to the city.

During the entire period of his apostolate in Cartagena Pedro Claver had followed the construction work with vigilant eye. At no time in the history of the mammoth project were less than twelve hundred Negroes employed upon it at once. Father Claver had watched these slaves at work — stripped to the waist, their ebony bodies dripping with sweat, their look dejected and forlorn. The day's labor began at cockcrow that it might be concluded before the intense heat of mid-afternoon. When they were released from their toil and had rested and refreshed themselves a little, the Apostle would gather as many of them as possible and teach and minister to them.

Claver realized that the souls of the Negroes were laden with far heavier chains than those borne over their shoulders as they dragged the great blocks from place to place. The granite was taken from old disused quarries near the sea. Heavy sand was transported with them. Much of this material was conveyed in strong raft-like boats, traveling constantly between the islands and the mainland. When these blocks were deposited on the shore they were drawn to their final destination in carts having two, sometimes four huge wheels. Sometimes the carts were drawn by oxen, more often by slaves. The strength of at least one hundred black men was required to drag the load to its place.

Father Claver had often seen a Negro drop to the sand, weakened to the point of unconsciousness by the strain of tugging, combined with the stifling heat, or even from a murderous kick administered by an overseer. When a slave showed the least disposition to fall behind he was speedily whipped into action and not infrequently to death.

Solicitous over this state of things Father Pedro left nothing undone to ensure the salvation of all newly transported blacks, should they be suddenly called from their miserable existence on earth.

The Apostle of Cartagena also conducted an intensive missionary work among the Spanish engineers belonging to the corps of one hundred and forty-five picked men in charge of the construction work. He often stopped to speak with them. If it happened that they were partaking of their ration of meat and yucca, with a coconut or panela cake as dessert, they would offer him a share. In that event he asked as a favor that he be allowed to accept it for his sick slaves.

When the priest had gone on, leaving the Spaniards his blessing and the promise of his prayers, they would converse together on the subject of their remarkable countryman. They marveled that this little priest was content to remain in a torrid and humid country, in a miserably unhealthful dwelling, to become the helper and companion of the ignorant and unprepossessing creatures so universally despised.

The sentinels, posted in their little boxes at frequent intervals along the walls, looked from their *guaridas* and saluted in response to Father Claver's genial nod and blessing. In his solitary cell each man looked forward with eagerness to the hour when the Apostle would pass that way. With him he brought a sense of cooling in the heat, of ease and comfort in the dreary season of rains, and, always, the spirit of his Lord and Saviour Jesus Christ. They remarked to one another that the walls of Cartagena would forever be impregnated with the virtues of the "Holy Father Pedro."

At midday the Heroic City slumbered in the gold of the

sun and the breath of the flowers. No wind idled through the Calle de la Media Luna or the Calle de San Ignacio, turning in to wander through the Calle de Santa Teresa and Santo Domingo where many of the finest Spanish houses were situated. No figure loomed on the sandy paths or fanned itself in the shade of the knotted old trees. Only a few black children played in the shelter of the mata-raton, mouse-killer, planted along the roadsides to afford relief from the sun's rays. The mata-raton was held in high favor; it was credited with keeping the mice, whose number was legion, at a distance. Like the white thoughts of the holy souls dwelling in the numerous cloisters of Cartagena were the small star-shaped flowers of the tumba-pared, an ubiquitous plant not generally appreciated, despite its loveliness, since it took root so tenaciously on the walls that it eventually caused them to crack.

The black children were pulling off the green fruit of the tumbapared to use as playthings; it was not edible and no one had been able to discover any good purpose it might serve. They passed small tongues restlessly over their lips as they remembered that the water boy had passed with his cart several hours before and would not come again until nightfall. Out of the goodness of his heart he would have dispensed a little of the precious liquid to his youthful acquaintances.

In the d'Urbina household a stillness reigned that was quite unlike the joyous activity long characteristic of the family.

Only the mistress of the mansion moved somberly through the deserted rooms. In a chamber long since abandoned by its former tenant she paused a very long time, beside the great high bed where her father, Don Juan d'Estrada, had breathed his soul into the keeping of its Maker.

Isabel touched the gaily colored blankets, woven in red, yellow, and purple wool in picturesque pattern. She had allowed no one to touch the bed since Don Juan's passing; when she deemed necessary she herself changed the linen cover of the mattress, stuffed with hay and wool, and the lace-fluted bedspread and pillow covers.

Beside the bed was a low chair; a little fresh straw had been sprinkled on the floor in front of it.

Isabel d'Urbina sat down in the little chair that seemed more suited to a doll than a full-grown woman. . . . At that moment a charge of artillery sounded from the harbor and bells began to ring all over the city.

It was the signal announcing the arrival of a treasure ship from Europe. Everyone would hurry to the shore to watch and wait for tidings of loved ones at home; to receive letters or merchandise and to welcome their kinsfolk to Cartagena's hospitable shores. Priests and religious, the nobility, and the common folk would alike hasten to the bay.

Father Claver might possibly be at his window, watching for a slave ship. Or he might be close to the old piers, attending to the sick slaves. Or at San Lazaro, outside the city walls — from that point it would be easy to sight a vessel while yet she was afar off.

But Isabel knew he would not leave his post to greet the treasure ship. He would go on, calmly, quietly, doing the task at hand. She was aware that her holy director allowed himself no natural satisfactions. Occasionally celebrated musicians would arrive at Cartagena from Spain. Always these visitors went to the Jesuit College and gave a concert to the Community. A number of distinguished guests would be present — only Father Claver would be missing. He never listened to discussions or news from the homeland or participated in these festivities.

A brother who had cared for the Apostle during an

illness had told of the penances Father Claver performed. Perceiving that he wore his hair shirt, although he was very weak, the brother had exclaimed:

"Ah, Father! What is this? How long are you to be harnessed in that fashion?"

The reply was: "Until death."

Another time the Apostle was running a high temperature, due to a fever contracted from a slave. The Provincial commissioned one of the fathers to remove the sick man's garments and arrange him more comfortably in his bed. The doctor was standing by. When Father Claver's clothing had been nearly removed and the man of science saw the sharp cords binding him, his eyes filled with tears.

"My dear Father!" he said, "How can you be other than ill when you treat yourself so badly? Are you not committing suicide when you do it?"

Despite Claver's protests a Negro undid the cords, but with the greatest difficulty.

Now that the sun of her life was beginning to descend, Isabel d'Urbina cherished all the more dearly every detail that concerned her Father in God.

Claver had replied to the brother who asked him how long he intended to ill-treat his body: "Until death" . . . Death. . . . The small word aroused a heavy sadness in Isabel's heart. Thinking about the cords which bound the servant of Christ, she asked herself what they had to do with fine linens and laces, with ruffled silk gowns, with emeralds and silver.

She regarded the floor of Don Juan's chamber intently, trying to picture the poor bed of the Apostle. Raised but a few inches above the rough boards, the hard leather would scarcely provide physical comfort. Brother Gonzalez had scoffed at Claver's "pillow," avowing that it was no better than a board, a place of concealment for a scourge.

The founder of Cartagena, Don Pedro de Heredia, was an intrepid warrior, brave and honorable according to his code. He had had his nose partly sliced off in a street brawl in Cadiz and submitted to have it operated upon without a murmur. They must have cut and burned and sewed considerably to have achieved so happy a result, the old historians said. And the victim had never uttered a groan. Heredia had lost an eye in another encounter and he had made sport of his mishap. He had astonished the Indians in America by removing the glass eye and then restoring it to its place, and they had deemed him a magician.

But Father Claver was much, much braver than the great general, Isabel thought. It was one thing to endure for the sake of an earthly triumph; to enjoy change of scene and thrilling hazards that would later redound to one's glory — and another thing to suffer and labor in poverty, humiliation and penance for the ulcerous and leprous blacks.

Father Claver had given Isabel his own points for meditation on the virtue of "long-suffering."

"When I am contradicted, why not do as the ass does? If he is abused or maltreated, he is silent. If forgotten or left without food; if made to work hard; if overladen, he is still silent — he does not complain. So ought a servant of God to act, saying with David: 'I am become as a beast of burden before Thee.' "

Isabel knew that not all his own brethren understood or approved of Father Claver's "excesses." Sometimes a brother would take pains to bring additional sufferings upon the innocent priest. For instance, for a time a certain Portuguese brother had been stationed at San Ignacio. This man was rude and rough in manner and speech. During his sojourn in Cartagena he had occasionally been sent out with Father Claver on his rounds. The unworthy brother would take extra pains to annoy, if possible, the

humble priest. Before starting out, he would keep him waiting unreasonably; again he would upbraid and censure him
as the two walked together. A hypocrite, a madman, a
fanatic — by these and other opprobrious names the
brother characterized the meek Apostle. . . . The fathers
never knew of this until it was too late to remedy the
wrong, for Father Pedro never spoke of anything done
against him. The Portuguese brother was later expelled
from the Society.

Isabel rose from the little chair as she saw Liseta at the
door of the chamber.

A visitor had arrived and wished to see Doña Isabel.
His name? Don Pedro Calderon.

Don Pedro was an officer of La Inquisición and a long-
time friend of the family. He conversed for a while with
the widow of Don Pedro d'Urbina on current affairs. At
the end he introduced the subject uppermost in his mind.

"Doña Isabel," he began, "I know of your great charities
and I have always admired and reverenced you for them.
Only yesterday I was speaking with Father Claver and he
told me he had long relied on you for help in his work,
and that you had never failed him."

Isabel murmured something, anything, while she waited
eagerly for the disclosure that was forthcoming.

Don Calderon was a blunt man. He came to the point
immediately.

"I have in mind to tell you of something that happened
yesterday," he said. "I was looking out of the palace windows, watching the rain — you remember? — when I saw
Father Claver coming along at a slow pace. I noticed how
thin and frail he seemed. It pained me, I assure you. . . ."
Isabel winced as her heart repeated the words her guest
had spoken: "thin . . . frail. . . ."

Calderon continued. "The sun broke through the
clouds, but the plaza remained flooded with water. Father

Claver was finding it extremely difficult to walk through the immense puddles without wetting his garments. I went out to him and said that I would order a chair to be brought at once, to convey him to the college.

"I even made so bold as to remind him that he was no longer young and that he should take this means to preserve his health. He replied: 'No, no; I will not allow that. A good fisherman ought not be afraid of wetting his feet.' "

Even so, Calderon had won out. It was a real triumph, for few in Cartagena could say that they had been able to change Father Pedro's mind. *"Muy mortificado!"* people would murmur and shake their heads. It seemed that the Apostle cared less for himself than any man they had ever known.

"Notwithstanding all the Father's objections," continued Don Calderon, "I had the chair brought around and got him into it. I was a little amused to see how ill at ease he looked! I am only afraid that, as a result of this 'indulgence' he performed some outrageous penance when he arrived home.

"I instructed the Negroes who brought Father Claver to San Ignacio to return the chair to me, and I sent a sum to its owner to pay the cost of it. You see, dear Isabel . . . I wanted to keep it in the family, so that, some day . . ."

Anew the grim thought of death presented itself to the lady upon whom Don Calderon looked with respect and admiration. . . . She put it from her, for one does not invite sorrow, and followed the caller to the door. The officer took up her dainty hand and kissed it reverently.

"Dear lady," he said, "I shall give you a confidence. It is a matter sacred to myself. Like you, I put myself under the guidance of Father Pedro, but only recently. I want to say to you that since I have gone to confession to him I have felt such a change in myself that I seem to be another man. I no longer have any difficulty in doing what I should do. And I have had the privilege of accompanying the Father a few times on an errand of charity. On the last occasion of the kind, when he went to visit a sick woman whom he greatly esteemed, he apparently restored her to health by his presence and his prayers. A member of the family has told me that, although her case was serious, she is now nearly well."

Both Isabel and Calderon would have been greatly interested in a conversation going on between two of the religious brethren of Father Claver just then.

In the College of San Ignacio the Rector was speaking with a visitor from Spain, Father José d'Urbina, formerly Claver's associate at Majorca.

Father Joseph was saying:

"I have never for a moment doubted the truth of what God made known to Brother Alfonso Rodriguez concerning Father Claver. I followed Claver, step by step in our early days, and I never witnessed anything in him that was not deserving of the highest crown."

Chapter VI

THE BROTHERS of San Juan de Dios, in charge of San Sebastiano's Hospital, had met with an unwonted distraction in the performance of their daily round of duties. It came about as the result of a recent visit of Father Pedro Claver, who on that occasion had left behind him something more than the odor of his virtues.

Early in the morning the Apostle had appeared on the premises in an old habit and the well-worn cloak. He carried a broom borrowed from the college, for the religious of San Sebastiano were so poor they lacked even the requisites for clean housekeeping. He had swept the corridors and tidied the rooms, performing all the labors he was accustomed to perform in the slave warehouses and huts.

Watching him at these tasks, which he accomplished with cheerfulness and alacrity, the Brother Superior remarked to another member of the Community: *"Muy mortificado, el Padre Claver!"* Yes; Father Claver was "very mortified," in soul and body.

The Apostle of the Slaves looked like an old man, now, although he was but three-score years. His body was shrunken and his brow more deeply lined. He was weakened and aged by toil and mortification, by long night vigils, by the denial of every instinct of self-gratification. The brothers of San Juan de Dios shook their heads sadly as they acknowledged that the little Jesuit far outstripped them in the practice of all the virtues.

When he had made his patients as comfortable as possible Claver went among them and spoke to each one in an effort to bring peace and happiness to their hearts. The childlike confidence the sick reposed in their Good Father had been expressed in many ways during the long period of his apostolate. He had never denied their legitimate requests. This day, however, was to remain forever in their memories as a day set apart from all others.

A sick Negro had told the Brother Superior of his desire for a certain species of fruit. The Negro knew that the brother would not fail to mention his request to the Apostle.

The fruit the sick man desired was then out of season. Although the superior was well aware of the fact he spoke of the matter to Father Claver.

The kindhearted Apostle responded instantly.

"I am going to get that fruit," he said. "You can rely on it, Brother. I shall find some place where it is to be found and bring you some."

Claver was gone about half an hour. When he returned he carried a small basket containing the most attractive fruit the brother had ever seen. Impossible as it seemed, it was the kind the sick Negro wished to have.

When Father Claver had finished his labors at San Sebastiano, the Superior spoke to another brother about the incident.

"I had sent everywhere, trying to find the fruit," he said. "But, as you know, Brother, it is not the season for it. Naturally, I was unsuccessful. . . . Father Claver alone knows how to produce it! I intend to make inquiries all over the city to see if by chance any is to be found. But" — the Superior paused, then added, significantly:

"I do not expect to find any!"

The Brother Superior carried out his intention. He made careful search for the fruit. There was absolutely none to be found in the markets of Cartagena.

He said no more on the subject. He was confirmed in his belief that Father Claver was not only a good man but a Saint. From that day he considered him as one.

Happy that he had been able to satisfy the desire of the sick Negro, Father Pedro left San Sebastiano. How many times the bruised feet had trod the paths leading from the various sections of the city to the little house which was his refuge and sanctuary, no one might tell. But the sight of the frail figure, always hurrying because there was so much work to be done, had become more important than anything else in Cartagena to Spanish and Negroes alike.

Many could remember Claver when he had first come to the Indies. They realized that he had altered greatly in the long years. They regretted this, for the brave buoyant spirit, the steadfast heart, the unfailing patience and fortitude of the Apostle had helped and strengthened and consoled people in all ranks of society. There still remained those who occasionally wounded the generous disciple of his Lord, who mocked at his consecrated labors and placed obstacles in the path of his holy ambitions. Nothing was able to shake his serene confidence in his mission or to evoke from him the least sign of anger or resentment. If, interiorly, Father Claver ever experienced the stern shock of disillusionment; if weariness of body or mind caused his staunch spirit to quail or droop ever so little, no one knew of it.

Occasionally the Apostle found it expedient to bring down the little whip, which he always carried under his habit, with more than usual vigor on the shoulders of a slave who was misbehaving. But he did not punish in anger. He realized that stern measures were needed to drive home the lesson he wished to impart.

As Claver entered the college, Brother Gonzalez informed him that a visitor waited in the parlor.

This visitor, a lady, had a disturbing circumstance to relate. A neighbor, another Spanish lady, had incurred heavy debts, owing to her son's bad management of her property. Creditors were besieging her on all sides, threatening her with dire penalties if she failed to pay at once. This situation had rendered her desperate.

"I am afraid she will do something to injure herself, Father," the visitor said. "If it is possible, I beg you to go to her. I know you can help her regain peace of mind."

The Apostle promised that he would go at once to see the unhappy woman.

The house he was about to visit was situated in the vicinity of the Governor's Palace, in the principal plaza of the city. When he arrived on the premises he found the slaves running about in extreme confusion and alarm. Seeing him whom they venerated and trusted above all others they burst into fervent expressions of thanksgiving. They informed Father Claver that their mistress had just gone to her room, declaring that she was about to put an end to her troubled existence by taking a dose of poison.

Claver ran up the stairs after one of the slaves. Already he could hear the sound of a key about to turn in a lock.

With firm grip the priest pushed open the door of a chamber. Looking on the unhappy woman, who was standing in the center of the elegantly appointed room, he said in compassionate voice:

"What is the matter, Señora?"

Overcome at the sight of the priest, the woman fell on her knees before him.

"Father! How glad I am to see you!" she said. "No doubt you are an angel, sent by God to save me!"

A few moment's questioning of the woman sufficed to tell Father Pedro that she was not thoroughly awake to the wrong she had been about to commit. When she had grown calmer he deemed it advisable to speak sternly to her. He pointed out that had she consummated her mad intention, she would have lost her soul. He told her he was certain that all the difficulties she had encountered were the result of her impious life, for she had concentrated on material things and neglected the spiritual.

"Enough of these offenses against your Creator," he said. "You belong to the devout sex and you are especially obligated to love and serve God. Yet you join with the impious to insult Him. For the sake of that Jesus who died to save souls, change your manner of living! God invites you to penitence and gives you grace for your sanctification. Do not continue to resist the kindness He shows you. If His loving appeals do not move you, at least fear His just punishments. Remember — life is fleeting as a shadow. Do not attach your heart to this miserable earth. Lift your eyes higher and direct them toward your true Country."

Father Claver's words were spoken in clear penetrating voice. The Spanish lady, providentially saved from a suicide's death, was at last thoroughly awake to the realization of her foolhardiness. She remained kneeling at the feet of the Apostle while he poured into her heart every counsel and encouragement to perseverance in a new and better life.

Father Claver grieved that he had been obliged to speak so severely to this soul. But a great Saint had said, "If you cannot cure the heart without afflicting it, that must be done, by all means."

The priest was drooping with fatigue when he left the house and turned in the direction of San Ignacio. Just then "Cartagenita" was lovely as a bride; a veil of delicate purple rested lightly upon her, embroidered by a maze of blossoms. As he came to the great walls, upon which a Spanish engineer stood watching the slaves at work, he saluted and blessed all — white men and black — and they saluted, each in his own fashion, and smiled at the gentle little priest.

The gallant son of Ana Sabocana would have found it restful to look across the sparkling waters just then — to watch the Negro mother, who, with her little child held close to her, lingered on the sands, pointing to a galleon anchored in the bay . . . to pause in some lonely spot along the shore and stretch his tortured feet to meet the trade wind . . . to drop below to the sands and, advancing to the very edge of the shimmering sea, dip them into the froth.

But Father Pedro did none of these things. Instead, he meditated on a motto by which he ruled all the actions of his life:

"I shall not seek in this world anything but that which Jesus Christ sought, namely, to sanctify souls, to suffer and even die for their salvation." . . . And continued on his way.

Passing a respectable-looking house on the Calle de la Media Luna, the priest was startled to hear cries of pain. He had heard that sound often, yet it always awakened a fresh horror in his soul.

He turned in at the gate leading to the house and went quickly up the path.

A Spanish mistress was beating her woman slave with a cruel-looking whip. This was a frequent occurrence in Cartagena. Father Claver never failed to offer eloquent pleas for forgiveness for the slaves when he happened to be in the vicinity of the disturbance, for he knew that too often they were punished without just cause.

When he entered the patio where the chastisement was being administered, the Spanish lady dropped the whip and loosed her hold on the slave. She appeared ashamed and lowered her eyes in presence of the reproachful Claver, whom she knew well.

In this instance the slave had deserved punishment, but Father Claver believed that he knew a better way to teach a lesson than by means of the whip. That way was a simple instruction on the love of God and the duty of all creatures, whether white or black, to obey and serve Him in all things. Only in rare instances was punishment necessary.

The captivating sweetness of the Apostle had its effect on mistress and slave alike. Both realized that his sole desire was that others should be happy and at peace with God.

When the slave had left the patio and he was alone with her mistress, Father Claver learned that the latter was anxious to help him in a project dear to his priestly heart. This project was the providing of a dowry for poor girls who wished to marry but had no funds for the purchase of a suitable trousseau. Improper dress was all too prevalent among the Negroes in Cartagena.

The lady advised Father Claver to appeal to the governor, a just and kindly man, asking a grant from the royal coffers for this purpose; for instance, a little of the tax moneys paid on exports and imports. When, some time afterward, he made the plea, he found the governor quite willing to grant his request. The official assured him that the other authorities, too, would gladly cooperate. Later these officials joined in making a personal tour of the city, asking donations from the wealthy families for this cause.

After leaving the house of the Spanish lady, Father Claver took out his little notebook and made an entry in it. This entry reflected the beauty and purity of Claver's soul. He was to carry the little notebook to his final hour on earth. Every inspiration received from heaven; every practical reflection, every point and principle he felt would better help him achieve his great end were faithfully recorded in its pages.

He could not know that long after his death this little
book was to be dearly cherished in the archives of the Jesuit
Province of Catalonia, his native place.

On this occasion the Slave of Slaves wrote down a resolve that he would aim to acquire a habit of thought,
feeling and aspiration, a second nature, as it were, whereby
all his efforts would be exclusively directed to the salvation
of souls, cost what it might — "even an ignominious and
cruel death."

Another resolve already entered in the little book was
that "neither heat nor cold, the late hour of the night or
the earliest of the morning; neither furious winds nor
deluging rains, dangerous roads or other difficulties, no
matter how great, shall stand in the way of the performance
of a duty to my fellow man."

The little Community at San Ignacio often remarked
that Father Pedro never exhibited any sign of fear or
resentment. No matter how arrogantly he might be be-
rated by the brutish slave masters for his charitable attentions to their Negroes; no matter what reproaches his own
brethren might heap upon him, he had never been known
to make any unkind retort.

When he had finished writing, Father Pedro replaced
the notebook next to his heart and continued on his way.

Above him the clouds drifted, like ships loosed from
anchorage, in the harbor of the sky. One, shaped like a
clumsy galleon, dipped low in the azure. As the Apostle
looked up to it, did the sudden remembrance of his dear
homeland come to him — for the phantom ship was drawing near. . . .

On the north of that beloved country the noble chain
of the Pyrenees formed a boundary for the Catalonian
Province; on the west was Aragon; on the south, Valencia;
on the east, the heavenly blue of the Mediterranean Sea.

But the heart of Pedro Claver had left Catalonia forever.

As the servant of the lowliest and most despised of human beings, Cartagena of the Indies would remain his place of exile. Not even his sacred bones would be returned to his native Spain, for he had irrevocably vowed all of him to the noble city of his adoption.

So the gray ship with the fleecy sails passed across the sky harbor and took its solemn departure.

Chapter VII

IN THE SILENT MANSION of the lamented Don Pedro d'Urbina on the Calle de la Media Luna two noble ladies sat over their evening meal.

Less frequently of late did visitors come to see the widow of the beloved and respected nobleman. The Cartageneans respected her wish to live a secluded life, almost that of a cloistered nun. Isabel dispensed her bountiful charities as before, but her heart was heavy because the hands through which those gifts had so often passed could no longer receive or distribute them. Father Pedro Claver was confined to his chamber most of the time, stricken by a disease contracted from a slave during the recent sad days of the pestilence. Only now and then could he rise from his bed to care for the sick Negroes. With the greatest difficulty he dragged himself, supported by a brother, to the altar to offer the Holy Sacrifice. His confessional was frequently occupied by another and the little gift table before it was empty.

Many others in Cartagena lay ill of the dangerous infection that had announced its coming a short time before it actually reached the city. Having ravaged and decimated Havana, Puerto Rico, and Vera Cruz, it progressed as far as the shores of Terra Firma, where it wreaked its greatest havoc, before going on to its final destination, the walled-in city by the beautiful, singing Caribbean.

At the first indication of its presence Father Claver had gone through the streets and along the seashore, warning all that danger was near and that it was advisable to prepare for any emergency, especially for the many deaths certain to result in a short time. He increased his penances and vigils, begging that God would spare the noble city. With breaking heart Isabel d'Urbina had watched the broken figure of the priest trudging past her door, sometimes drenched with the rain, sometimes scorched by the tropical heat, yet seeming to be wholly unmindful of the weather. She knew he was going to the bedside of a poor sinner, or, perhaps a dying leper or some other forlorn soul who had need of his ministrations before departing this life.

Sometimes the street was strangely empty — then Father Claver was penetrating into country places or passing along the seacoast, seeking abandoned Negroes in order to give them his priestly help. Traveling always on foot, he crossed rude hills, climbed rocks covered with briars and brambles and often waded, the water and mud almost to his knees, through bogs and ravines in the forests. His meals were taken in the poorest of the Indian or Negro cabins; they consisted of coarse bread made from Indian corn or a little rice cooked in salted water.

His interpreter had scolded him for refusing any comfort to his weakened body and had tried to persuade him to take some nourishment.

"Not yet; today I have performed no service for God," the Apostle invariably replied.

Sometimes Father Pedro found himself in a thicket of palm and banana trees where the mass of scarlet blooms on the many flowering bushes contrasted brilliantly with the vivid greens of the forest glade. He walked on the very trail of Don Pedro de Here,dia, who had made so many journeys into the interior of New Granada. He walked over the desecrated graves of Indians, buried long before, from which the intrepid Conquistador had removed the silver and other treasures. The conical mounds were long since trampled over and heavy growths of creepers now trailed over the resting places of a primitive and greatly wronged people. Sometimes Father Claver paused beside a caño, a running stream or backwater in the wood, to erase the marks of his toilsome pilgrimage from his hands and face.

At the command of his Superior, the valorous missionary had returned to Cartagena. When he entered the little house of his brethren in the Calle de San Ignacio, they realized how greatly he had suffered during his journeying. His flesh bore marks of thorns and brambles and the sting of many venomous insects. But the perennial smile was still on Claver's lips. He was satisfied, because he believed that he had visited every grove and coppice where a fugitive black man might be hiding out and prepared his soul for God. Father Claver declared to the Superior that his own sins had brought this pestilence upon his beloved Cartagena. The Superior allowed the remark to pass unanswered. But to one of the other fathers he said:

"I think it well to administer the Holy Viaticum to Father Pedro. I don't like his look."

The father replied: "At least he will be obliged to rest for a while. But I think Cartagena will not yet be deprived of his services."

Lying on the hide mat in a corner of his chamber, the Slave of the Slaves smiled radiantly when his Divine Lord was carried to him. He was unwilling to remain in a reclining posture in such august circumstances. To his eager request that he be allowed to rise and prostrate himself on the floor in presence of his Eucharistic King, the answer was: no. The invalid was so weak that the father who brought him the Blessed Sacrament feared he might expire, should he make the effort.

Like a simplehearted child Father Claver acquiesced in the decision. . . . Strange, strange it seemed to be lying there, helpless, waited on by others!

After he had received the Viaticum, he said, with tears moistening his cheeks:

"Almighty God will no longer make use of me, because I have been the most unworthy of His ministers."

All his brethren in the room were deeply affected by this humble avowal, which they knew to be far from the actual fact.

Later in the day Brother Gonzalez looked in to inquire whether Claver needed anything.

No. He had everything necessary, and it was far too much for one who deserved nothing at all.

"Father, you will pray for all the sick in Cartagena?" Brother Gonzalez asked — for the list of plague victims was steadily growing.

"Very willingly, Brother," answered the invalid. "I was just doing so when you came in."

From the Jesuit Superior, who had called to acquaint her of Claver's illness, Doña Isabel d'Urbina learned of all these happenings. Her distress was very acute. Her faithful Don Pedro had gone to his eternal rest, following her venerated father. Now Father Claver was very ill. . . .

César, Don Pedro d'Urbina's favorite mount, was suffering from a strange distemper that had manifested itself a few hours after his master's interment in the cemetery of Cartagena. Liseta had shaken her head dubiously as she recounted how the noble brute had refused to take food from the time he ceased to look for his master. He recovered a little but he was not the same. The two black servitors were deeply distressed lest the passing of César, who had been closer to Don Pedro than anything save Isabel herself, should bring their mistress to a still more pitiable state of dejection.

Isabel toyed with her spoon as she remembered with consolation that many Masses were being said all over the city from time to time, for Don Pedro's repose. Only that morning one of the spiritual sons of San Luis Beltran had stood at the altar and offered the Spotless Victim for her beloved.

Jeromina complained that her sister had eaten nothing. Isabel pushed aside her favorite dish, an omelet with fried sweet potatoes: *"Yo no puedo comer!"* she said, "I cannot eat it." The younger sister whispered to Liseta, who stood near, watching anxiously: *"Leveselo!"* "Take it back!"

Similar incidents had occurred all too frequently of late. It seemed that the bright serene spirit of Doña Isabel was near to breaking through the fragile shell of her body.

Soon blessedly welcome news came.

Father Claver had come back to this world after hovering for some time on the brink of another. He had gained a certain measure of energy and seemed on the road to at least partial recovery.

However, the doctors had told the Superior that the Apostle would never fully regain his health. His hands and feet had been seized with a violent trembling. Only in one circumstance did this disappear — when Claver used the discipline, as he continued faithfully to do.

Isabel was greatly consoled. The thought that her saintly Father was spared for a while longer to those who sorely needed him brought infinite solace to her heart. But the joy was tempered by the remembrance of his infirmity which seemed destined to be permanent.

One question trembled on her lips.

Would Father Claver be able to . . . to . . .

The Father Superior, to whom she spoke, understood.

He replied: "Father Pedro cannot say Mass regularly. But I think he will be able to care for a few of his penitents. The affair is in God's hands. He has spared our Good Father a long time, despite his great labors and mortifications. Perhaps many years will yet be granted to him. Who knows?"

Who . . .? Only One. That One was God.

When the Father Superior had gone Isabel sank into a great armchair in the sitting room of the mansion where she could look out into the patio, now shining brightly after a day of rain.

"My God, I love Thee much, very much. . . ." She repeated over and over the words so frequently on the lips of her Father in Christ.

"Much . . . very much. . . ." Those words were a great part of a woman's life, she thought. Things that pressed on a woman's heart were never little, or if little to a man, were to her who was gifted with a more sensitive nature, a clearer intuition, almost too poignant to bear.

Isabel had traveled very far, since her marriage to Don Pedro d'Urbina, without leaving Cartagena of the Indies. Her thoughts strayed now to the preparations for her bridal. Wearisome in the extreme it had been for the laughing girl to stand for the final fitting of her wedding gown. She recalled how she had anxiously inquired about the pattern of the skirt, after the fashion of every Spanish maiden about to be given in marriage. "Is it wide enough?" The outer skirt covered numerous inner ones, all flounced and ruffled. The velvet bodice, very tight, revealing the lovely lines of her figure, was embroidered with jewels and silver lace. . . . Now the once merry Isabel blushed, recalling her chagrin on the way to church as she thought that her mantilla hid too much of the charm of her bridal gown.

Centuries in the past that radiant day now seemed, with

the wonderful celebration that followed the marriage, music and dancing and feasting far into the morning of the following day. Now, other memories were infinitely more precious. Isabel's long dark lashes drooped over her pallid cheek as a far different picture presented itself to her mind.

Father Claver, enjoying a festival with his newly baptized Negroes. . . . First he cleaned and swept the untidy pen where the cermonies were to be held. Then he sprinkled the premises with perfumed waters. Then, with exquisite care, he arranged a simple little altar, covered it with clean cloths, and set upon it the chalice for the Precious Blood. . . .

When the sacred ceremonies were over, on shoulders that bore the marks of a lash so constituted that it sought out every nerve and fiber of a man's flesh and set them tingling with pain . . . he had placed a basket of goodies and had gone among his children, distributing them.

Father Pedro had drooped from day to day, even before the fatal sickness gripped him as the mata-raton gripped the walls that ran past the blue and mauve and pink colored houses. Yet God had deigned to spare him for a while to those who loved and needed him.

The Apostle had built on the structure begun by his saintly predecessor, Father Alfonso de Sandoval, in the soul of a noble Sevillana, Isabel d'Urbina. And she had given that generous response both saintly men expected of her.

First — to God; she had Father Claver to thank most for that. He had continued the work on the strong foundation blocks set in place by Father Alfonso. The Apostle had followed a plan with painstaking care and zeal, as the Spanish engineers followed a plan in the erection of the mighty walls about the city. He had watched diligently to ensure that every detail was fulfilled in minutest way.

Second — to Don Pedro d'Urbina Isabel had dedicated

her whole being, and her great love and devotion; to the worthy partner of her days and ways, by whose side she had walked proudly and innocently during the years of their ideally happy wedded life.

Third — to Cartagena of the Indies, whose flowerlike grace and charm and whose dignified and romantic heritage had claimed more and more of her as time went on. Today, after nearly four decades, some of the gracious landmarks had melted into decay. The small demonlike fingers of the tumbapared had wormed their way into the plaster of the stately mansions in the Calle de la Media Luna and the other streets of the city. The grim roots of the great trees, stretching so far into the soil, had grown grayer and more gaunt, as much else that Isabel knew and loved. The white stars that matted the foliage of the tumbapared so thickly seemed to the lonely widow of Don Pedro d'Urbina, when she was borne past them in her chair, more fragile, more elusive, more deceiving in their promise of enduring beauty. For no one who was unfamiliar with the plant could dream of the destructive force that worked beneath those seemingly helpless little stars of silk. . . . They no longer brought to Isabel a sensuous pleasure as in her youth, but a little fear and a great longing.

Heaven itself, as the greatly altered Carmen de Badajos remarked to Isabel, however infinitely desirable it was, seemed unreal at times, for one was not permitted even a fleeting glimpse of its never-ending joys. Father Claver had reminded Carmen that Faith alone could penetrate that region of the blessed and that by Faith we merit their eternal reward.

Father Claver knew. Teresa de Cepeda y Alhumada knew. Ignacio de Loyola and Francisco de Xavier knew. These heroic friends of God comprised Isabel's prayer court.

The bereaved lady knew that in his loyal and unselfish

heart Father Claver thought of all who believed in him
and followed his counsels. Now they were united in prayer
for his complete recovery. He was aware that could not
be. But the zealous petitions would effect a beautiful
purpose. They would be answered in another way. Many
souls would be purified by means of them as well as by
the tears and vigils of faithful and devoted hearts.

Soon the object of so many prayers and tears had so
far recovered from his malady that, after being assisted to
rise and dress by a negro boy, he could drag himself into
the church to hear Mass and communicate. His confessor
had wished to come to Claver's room when his services
were desired; Claver insisted that the order be reversed,
saying that it was unseemly that a priest should wait upon
him.

"Where is Father Pedro?" Brother Gonzalez would inquire of the negro attendant. Usually the answer was:
"He is hearing confessions in the church."

The sacristan had asked the Father Superior whether he
might grant the Apostle's request to be called whenever
anyone came seeking a confessor at night. Claver was
anxious that they be sent to his room, for he wished to
expend some of his boundless energy in helping them.

The answer was — yes. The Superior could not find it
in his heart to refuse a favor he knew would bring great
happiness to his spiritual son.

On a few occasions Father Pedro had himself carried
to the huts of some Negroes who had recently come to
Cartagena from Arrais and who knew nothing of the true
religion. He looked eagerly for an interpreter who knew
the tongue of these Negroes; it was difficult to find one,
but he never complained of the anxiety the delay caused
him. When finally one was found, the Apostle was
overjoyed.

Doña Isabel sometimes wondered about the slave boy

commissioned to look after the wants of the holy man. She knew Father Claver would not complain if he was mistreated or even abandoned in time of need. Her woman's intuition told her that all was not well in this regard. . . .

Isabel was somewhat comforted when she opened her book of devotions and read the counsels written on a little slip of paper by her holy Director himself:

"Stamp, Lord, Thy wounds on my heart, that in them I may find pain and love; pain, to suffer for Thee all kinds of pain; love, to despise for Thee all inordinate affection."

Chapter VIII

AT THE FOOT of the Baluarte de San Antonio green and yellow lizards dozed in the heat. A few figures moved in the distance, passing through the arch beneath the chapel of the Convent of Santo Domingo in one or the other direction — to the sea — which they must skirt to reach the Street of the Half-Moon, or to the Jesuit College, three blocks distant. Thousands of times Father Pedro Claver had walked beneath the chapel on his way to the slave pens or to the Hospital of San Lazaro. Now the tired feet would never again make this journey of merciful love.

The little house of the Jesuit fathers in the Calle de San Ignacio was very still. No call of cocinera sounded high among the palms in the patio where the slaves had ceased to gather for their daily instruction. No gold-robed butterfly flitted about the cloisters like golden prayers winging their way to the House of Gold where all lovely things are finally closeted with God.

The Apostle of the Negroes lay on his bed of death in the chamber over the portery, very weary after a journey that had consumed nearly forty years.

Pedro Claver, of the Society of Jesus, had started out from Sevilla one morning in April, on his way to heaven. He had stopped most of the time in Cartagena of the

Indies, from whose shores he had looked often to the Ivory and Gold Coasts and to Guinea. Now the time of departure was at hand. All his baggage was packed and ready, his good and loving deeds for his Crucified Master. Countless times the pallid lips had formed the words: "O, my Jesus! My God, crucified for me! I love Thee much; yes, very much, with all my heart!"

Much, very much, had he loved, and now the time of loving on this earth was nearly over. Pedro Claver, Apostle of Cartagena, Slave of the Slaves, was soon to know how the blessed love in heaven.

While he was still able to go about, he had visited Doña Isabel d'Urbina, carried to the house by two of the brothers. Alone with his faithful disciple and friend he told her the day and the hour in which he would leave this world.

Isabel had wept without restraint. "Father, as long as I may have the happiness of your direction, I want no one else," she said.

It cost Father Claver much to witness Isabel's distress. Yet he repeated his statement — that she would never again see him alive, because his death would occur shortly. He promised that he would not forget her, who was so dear to him, before God.

The Apostle's face was sunken and aged as he lay quiet on his uncomfortable bed. Of late he had not been able to leave it; to go forth at midnight, down cloisters lighted only by a great round moon, bearing a wooden cross on his shoulders and, with a crown of icaco thorns encircling his brow, run to and fro in the ardor of his desire to more closely approach his Suffering Redeemer.

He would never again celebrate on this earth the dearly loved feasts of his Lady Mary, Mother of his Lord. He had said to her: "My good Mother! I beg you to teach me how to love your Son! Obtain for me one spark of that pure love that always burned in your heart for Him. Or, rather, lend me your heart, so that I may at least love Him worthily."

On the previous day Father Pedro had enjoyed a little treat that had consoled, even ravished his childlike soul. A band of musicians, Negroes who had often accompanied him to San Sebastiano's to play for the sick, had come into the patio and serenaded him. He deemed himself unworthy of the attention but he accepted it humbly as one more evidence of God's love for "a poor sinner such as I am."

About Father Pedro's neck was a treasured medal of his illustrious Patron, San Ignacio de Loyola. It was worn quite thin from being pressed so often in the frail fingers and to the virginal lips. Now his hands were folded over it as he prayed to his great Founder for the graces he desired.

Shortly before, the Spanish fleet, under command of the Marquis de Montalegre had dropped anchor in the harbor of Cartagena. The sound of rejoicing all over the city penetrated to the sick chamber. Father Claver was instantly on the alert. Was this excitement the signal of the arrival of a slave ship? In that event he must try to dress himself and go down to see what could be done for the Negroes on board.

The black boy who waited on the Apostle so wretchedly deigned to impart the desired information.

The ship had brought to the Indies a member of the society, Father de Farigna. This father had been chosen to succeed the dying Apostle in the work of evangelizing the slaves.

When he heard the news Father Claver raised his eyes to heaven and prayed for a short time. He then announced that he must go at once to welcome and congratulate the newly arrived missionary.

With the greatest difficulty he dragged himself to Father

de Farigna's room. He prostrated himself before his successor and, kissing his feet with the greatest respect, congratulated him on the "glorious office" assigned to him.

"But, Father, I have done nothing as yet. How do I merit this respect?" Father de Farigna asked in surprise. "Please tell me your name."

The name —? Ah! It was only "Slave of the Slaves." There was no other. What more beautiful title could any man bear?

Father de Farigna in turn knelt at the feet of the Apostle and asked his blessing.

"Father," he said, "I shall always look on you as my teacher and guide."

In his extremity a sore trial was at hand for Father Claver. He learned with dismay that a part of the college, located above the city walls, was to be demolished immediately — by order of the King.

Several other members of the Community were ill in that part of the house just then. Claver felt that the sight of his brethren being expelled from their lodgings, their only home for so long a time, would be too painful for him to bear. He asked God to spare him this cross — to take him quickly to Himself.

The dying priest confided a certain desire to Brother Gonzalez. It was that he might be buried at the foot of his confessional where he had spent so many fruitful hours teaching his Negroes the way to happiness here and hereafter.

Brother Gonzalez knew the Superior would not permit that the Apostle should be interred in the lowliest spot in the sacred place.

"No! No!" Brother replied, vehemently. "It shall be in the chapel of our Lord."

When he had helped Father Pedro to his bed and covered him with the old patched cloak, Brother begged:

"Father, when you reach heaven, please recommend the city of Cartagena to God. And, Father, please never forget this country which you have watered with your sweat and where you have gained so many souls and won such great merit."

Brother was deeply moved by Claver's reply.

"I have lost all merit by my impatience in suffering."

Brother Gonzalez felt certain that the Apostle had received intimation of his future reward, for he spoke with serene confidence of the peace and joy awaiting him in eternity.

Below stairs the sorrowing Brother told the Community all that had passed between Father Claver and himself. In his simplicity Brother suggested a plan by means of which the Apostle would be reminded of his brethren in Cartagena when he should have entered into the joy of his Lord. It was that all the religious in the house should write their names on a piece of paper, and the paper be given to Father Claver before his passing from this life. This plan was carried out.

Two visitors from the outside world were admitted to the chamber. The first was the commander of the Spanish fleet, the Marquis de Montalagre; before embarking for the return voyage he wished to pay his respects to his beloved friend.

The Father Superior conducted the Marquis to Claver's side and left him there.

The Marquis seated himself on a wooden stool beside the bed. He regarded the priest with a look of sorrow and compassion, not unmixed with awe. He pitied the poor body that had suffered such severe punishment at the will of its master. De Montalagre, who was accustomed to use perfume on his handkerchiefs, admired the fragrant odor he believed emanated from the flowering shrubs beneath the windows. A moment later he perceived that it came from the cloak, laid over the wasted form of the Saint.

"I have come to ask your prayers for my safe and prosperous journey home," the Marquis began. "Many perils confront my ship and my men, with so many enemies of Spain riding the seas. I shall feel secure if you pray for us, Father."

The Apostle replied, in a feeble voice, that the prayers would be faithfully recited.

Had the Marquis deemed it fitting he would have asked for the faded old cloak, in order to take it with him to Catalonia where it would be cherished by Father Claver's relatives and no doubt, work miracles! He did not broach the subject, however, knowing that the priest would not permit it, and, also, that the fathers would wish to retain it as a sacred souvenir. De Montalagre made a different request — he asked for a memento of the Apostle to keep as token of a venerated friendship.

Claver answered that a poor man like himself had nothing fit to offer a nobleman. Then he remembered that the Marquis had married a niece of Father Francisco Borgia, second General of the Jesuits, and that it would be appropriate to offer him a medal of San Ignacio de Loyola.

He handed the medal to his visitor. With it he bestowed a last blessing. He then bade the commander farewell.

Another, who had been anxiously waiting for admittance to the little chamber, took the place of the Marquis. This other was a member of the Franciscan Order; he had been Father Claver's penitent for many years.

The two congenial souls spent a long time together, conversing on spiritual topics.

"I regret that your holy house is to be partly demolished," the Franciscan said. "But the King's orders may not be gainsaid. How soon will the workmen begin, Father?"

"Very soon. I shall not live to see it," Claver replied.
"How is that? For I am told they are to start tearing
down the walls tomorrow."

The dying Apostle reiterated that he would not live to
see it. "Because," he naïvely added, "I have begged our
Lord to call me to Himself before the work begins. In His
goodness He has promised to do so."

When he had made the last confession to the Apostle he
would ever make, the spiritual son of Saints Francisco
and Pedro left the room, bowed in grief.

The Slave of the Slaves had no further work to do. No
more visitors would be admitted save the Divine Redeemer
in the holy Viaticum. But first Claver asked Brother
Emmanuel Lopez to destroy his signature on all the papers
he had prepared for the Negroes, as proof that they had
been to confession.

Brother appeared to agree to this. When he made known
the request to the Superior the latter denied it.

"Collect all those papers and bring them to me!" he
ordered. "I intend to keep one for myself. After Father
Pedro's death I shall distribute the others among the
people. The autograph of a saint is precious, you know."

Brother Lopez believed that he did know.

Chapter IX

SUNDAY MORNING, the sixth day of September, of the year 1654.

The tropical rains had nearly spent themselves during a long humid season. Now they were moving out to the end of the low coastal region west of the Magdalena River on which Cartagena was situated. The sun gilded the arches supporting the upper gallery of the cloisters, whose floor had so often felt the impress of the long beam of a cross as Father Pedro Claver trod the Way of Sorrow. The Apostle had been carried to the chapel to receive Holy Communion. As he was borne past the sacristy on the way back to his room he asked a question of the brother in charge.

"Brother," he said, "I am going to die. What do you wish of me in the next world?"

At first startled, the brother recovered himself and replied:

"That you recommend this city and house to God, Father."

Claver promised that he would do so.

Helped back on his hard bed the dying man lay quiet all day, engaged in tender communications with his Lord. Toward evening, when the trade wind swept in from the sea, a fever, aggravated by Father Claver's fervor in his prayers, set in. It was evident that all remedies were now useless.

He remained in that condition until the next morning. When the infirmarian went to his bedside he found that his patient had lost the power of speech. Yet his lips seemed to be trying to form words. . . .

"Jesus! Jesus! I love you much, very much!"

The doctor bent down to listen for the beating of the generous and long-suffering heart. Some strength yet remained in the wasted body. It was not quite time for Father Pedro to go "home."

Doctor Adan Sobo passed through the deserted corridors with slow, uncertain step. He was saddened by the thought that he would never again be called upon to exercise his faithful ministrations in behalf of his venerated friend. He glanced down at his homemade comfortable shoes and contrasted them with the broken alpargates he had noticed beside the bed. Thinking of the mortifications and penances borne by Father Claver for the salvation of so many in Cartagena, the doctor could not feel that he himself deserved the kind words said of him by those who trusted to his skillful care:

"He is a Saint! He will go to heaven with his shoes on!"

He thought that the blessed inhabitants of heaven would rejoice to welcome Father Claver, worn-out alpargates and all!

The Apostle would be missed in every circle. He had done much, very much to bring the sweet comforts of Christ to souls, driving out the old superstitions to which many had clung all their lives. Father Claver had indignantly protested against the practice of putting parts of dead birds, tied up in a little bag, near the sick in the hope of curing them by that expedient. He had abolished the practice of reciting the Magnificat in reverse for three consecutive hours at the head of the sickbed, meanwhile making weird signals that must not be interrupted. The doctor had Father Pedro to thank that those afflicted with eye disorders now sent for him instead of spending their time rolling their eyes in the direction of a rooster. . . .

Leaving the premises, Doctor Sobo proceeded to a house where he was assured of a royal welcome, in the advent of a new little life into the world. He stood outside the door, according to the custom, while the hired musicians played three pieces of music . . . today his heart was not in a joyous mood; he was not prepared for his triumph. At the conclusion of the third piece, he went into the house.

When he reappeared, he had wonderful news to relate . . . not one, but two little ones had come to gladden and bless the home of a worthy Spanish couple. . . . His face, however, was not wreathed in smiles, and he had little to say in response to the congratulations of the neighbors. He was thinking of the life that was ebbing away, so quietly, so lonely, perhaps — in the old college; for was not death always lonely, even to the saints?

Into the basket which the doctor carried, the good people of Cartagena dropped foodstuffs, as reward for his faithful services and a token of their esteem. Today he did not feel happy that he was assured of some special delicacies when he should sit down to dine. He was remembering the heavy baskets Father Claver had carried during the long years, in the rains and the heats, on shoulders never built for burdens of that kind.

For the last time the kindhearted man of medicine had seen a light of recognition on the face of his friend. Henceforth he would have to go on without him. But he knew that Father Pedro would not forget those dear to him when he was in heaven.

"Buen viaje, amigo mio!" Doctor Sobo had said, upon going out of the pathetically poor little sick chamber.

But his old friend had not heard the words, wishing him a safe journey — into eternity.

Chapter X

FROM THE WALL of Father Pedro's chamber the quiet face of Brother Alfonso Rodriguez looked down on a beloved brother and disciple in Christ whose long self-denying apostolate was swiftly drawing to its close.

There was no light in the room save that which streamed in from the sky — it was a clear night of stars above the Caribbean. The negro boy, who slept in the room, was gratified to think he would no longer be obliged to replenish the candles, two very small candles, which must be exchanged for others when they had burned low in their sockets. The black boy found this task very inconvenient and distasteful. Too indolent to rise and perform his duty when the candles had burned out, it cost him no qualms of conscience when, awaking from sleep, he would notice that red tongues of fire were casting a bright glow on the ceiling. And he would say:

"Where did the candles come from? Who put them there?"

The Slave of the Slaves, lying very still, his hands clasped on his breast over his crucifix, his eyes searching the great wounds of his Lord in the picture at the foot of his bed, would smile as he replied, in feeble voice:

"Sleep, sleep, child. Don't trouble yourself about that."

Now, the last candles were flickering out with a faint

lingering radiance. That did not matter, for soon Father Claver's eyes would be closed for always.

In the narrow street before the college Negro children were crying: "The Saint is dying! The Good Father is dying! Soon he will leave us!"

The report of Father Claver's sinking condition spread with lightning rapidity throughout all Cartagena. In a short time a great crowd had gathered outside the lowly residence of the Jesuits. They clamored to be admitted that they might venerate their beloved Father once more before he was taken from them. Priests and religious, government officials and nobles, and hundreds of negro slaves were in the crowd.

The Father Superior acceded to the plea. However, as evening fell and the crowds outside the college became denser, he judged it expedient to close the doors and deny admittance to any others. This decision, however, proved useless, for, as the Negroes pressed closer, the door gave way and they were able to achieve their yearning desire. In groups, as they could gain admittance to the tiny chamber, they knelt about the dying Saint. Kissing his hands and feet, they strove with one another to gain possession of some relic to take with them as a hallowed souvenir of their Good Father. The Community was helpless in the face of this tumultuous, albeit childlike devotion which was not to their liking since they were afraid it might disturb the Apostle. However, Father Claver remained motionless, his eyes closed, making no sign that he was aware of what was going on.

Soon the various removable articles in the room had been seized by the Negroes, with the exception of the hide mat serving for a bed, upon which Father Claver lay, the coverlet over his wasted form and the picture of Brother Alfonso on the wall which one of the fathers had found necessary to protect as it was about to be carried off. Only when all his black children had been able to touch their Father and friend and to pour out their heart-rending lamentations at his side, were they prevailed upon to leave.

Doña Isabel d'Urbina and several other Spanish ladies who had long been Father Claver's penitents had obtained permission to send two artists to make portraits of the saintly priest as he lay motionless, slowly breathing out his angelic soul to God. The artists experienced no difficulty in their task, save that now and then tears fell on their palettes and mingled with the colors.

Father Pedro had declared that he would depart this life on a feast day of our Lady. All the Community felt certain this prediction would be fulfilled.

The Father Superior had paid a visit to Claver shortly after midnight, September 8, the feast of our Lady's Nativity. At that time the prayers for a departing soul were recited. None of the fathers or brothers went away after that, for all wished to be present when a Saint took flight to heaven.

At two o'clock in the morning, when the watchman was making his rounds of the city walls and the Community were invoking the Sacred Names of Jesus and Mary for the well-being of his precious soul, Father Pedro Claver opened his eyes and, with a smile, partly raised his hand in blessing.

A moment after, the heroic Apostle slept in Christ.

For a short time after death the sacred body, emaciated and worn by labors and austerities, appeared shrunken and aged. But soon it assumed an entirely different aspect, as all in the room observed. The hands and feet that had served the Lord so zealously remained flexible — but none was surprised at that. Father Pedro's face, too, was freed from the lines graven there by pains of soul and body; by the ceaseless combat to suppress every purely human instinct and desire. So calm it was that it was not difficult for his sorrowing brethren to picture Claver already in the arms of Him whom he had so royally served and imitated.

Reverend hands robed the precious remains in the sacred vestments worn at the holy altar in the Mass which the Apostle had said daily at high noon. Then began the preparations for the funeral.

Very early the city began to take on the appearance of a great religious holiday. Processions of religious robed in black or white or brown passed from their monasteries through the streets and into the college of the Jesuit Fathers, to view the blessed body and pray beside it.

Bells tolled solemnly in every bell tower. From the Monastery of Santa Cruz de la Popa on its pine-garlanded pedestal the sad music was borne far out to sea so that officers and crews of many ships wondered what was happening in the old walled-in city. It came from the Convent of San Francisco, close to the Plaza one day to be dedicated to the Independence of New Granada when that colonial holding had won her freedom from Spain; from San Augustino, consecrated a few years before the young and ardent Claver had come to Cartagena of the Indies; from Santa Teresa, where the spiritual daughters of a valiant Spanish mother knelt in prayer on the cold stone floors of their cells; from Santa Clara, where the daughters of Doña Catalina Cabrera united in prayer for the Father whose deeds they knew so well. Only five years before Claver's solemn profession the Spanish noblewoman, Doña Catalina, had founded her convent, taking with her into the strict enclosure three others equally distinguished; Suor Catalina de la Concepción, Suor Inez de la Encarnación, and Suor Leonor de los Angeles. In spirit these cloistered virgins had followed Father Pedro through the city whose streets they might never tread; into the holds of the slave ships, into the slave warehouses; they had stood beside him in spirit as he taught the ignorant and helpless Negroes in the thickets of the icaco trees or in the shadow of the Government Palace. Through the long years these chosen ones had prayed and sacrificed for the success of Father Claver's work. Now the sorrowful word had been flashed to these, who knew not the outer world, that their Apostle was no more on earth. And, as they thought of him already enjoying the Beatific Vision, they offered their stainless petitions to rather than for their illustrious countryman.

When one mellow pensive note had died away in the bell towers another broke on the air, dispelling the silence that otherwise rested over the stricken city.

Fathers and brothers at San Ignacio rejoiced when they learned that a fitting shrine was being prepared for the entombment of their Saint. Doña Isabel d'Urbina, the most cherished and loyal of all Father Claver's friends, had sent word that a magnificent casket of cedarwood, exquisitely fragrant and polished to a brilliant sheen; lined with richest materials and fringed with gold, with handles and trimmings of the finest gold, would be sent shortly to the residence of the fathers. Doña Isabel humbly begged that her Father in God might be placed in this shrine and when the funeral Mass had been sung and the coffin sealed, be interred within it, in the chapel of our Lord, near the altar, to await the Resurrection.

The authorities of Cartagena conferred together as to the best means of showing reverence and honor to the dead Apostle. It was not meet, they said, that this deeply venerated citizen, "man of God and angel of charity," should be laid to rest without receiving the public homage his life and works merited.

Don Pedro, Duke of Estrada, sent a large sum of money to the Jesuit fathers, requesting that a supply of candles be procured and kept lighted all during the period of the funeral services. Don Pedro de Zapata, Governor of Cartagena, assembled the magistrates of the city in his palace and proposed that the funeral expenses should be paid from the public coffers. "For," he said, "it is only fitting that we should show our gratitude to Father Claver for his distinguished services to us."

The other officials gladly agreed to the proposal. Two emissaries were immediately dispatched to San Ignacio, requesting the Superior to defer the burial of Father Claver until the following day. Meanwhile, the Governor made known his desire that the holy remains should be taken to the church and left there sufficiently long so that all the people might bid farewell to their venerated Father.

These plans were carried out, although in the tropical climate of Cartagena such delay in the interment of the dead was most unusual.

Only priests were permitted to touch the handsome shrine in which Father Claver rested. The ministers of Christ bore it on their shoulders into the church and set it down before the altar where the Saint had said Mass for nearly forty years. It was difficult to keep the crowds in line; all wished to lay rosaries or medals or other objects of piety on the hands of the dead Apostle, or even to kiss those members, now flawless and perfect after their years of arduous labors. In his apostolate of charity Father Pedro had gravely ill-used those delicately formed members; he had forced them to carry heavy baskets of provisions for the sick; to wield mop and broom; to anoint running sores; to wipe leprous foreheads; to busy themselves in the heat and the storm; to permit themselves no rest while there was work to be done for the abandoned blacks. It was well known in Cartagena that Father Pedro had carried on his back, countless times, an aged and sick Negro the entire fifteen blocks that lay between the harbor and the Hospital of San Lazaro, outside the city walls.

Toward nightfall many Negroes arrived at the church; they carried ribbons, pieces of cotton cloth, beads, and whatsoever other similar articles they possessed in order to lay them on their dead Father.

The Prior of the Augustinians with six of his religious came to relieve Father Pedro's brethren of their long watch. They wished to cover the holy body with a black velvet pall until the hour of the funeral Mass. But this the people would not permit. So the Father of all Cartagena lay at peace in Doña Isabel's costly shrine, smiling as he had smiled during his lifetime on all in the city.

The Augustinian Fathers rejoiced when the coveted honor of conducting the funeral services was awarded to them for their zeal and charity in assisting Father Claver's brethren. The privilege of preaching the eulogy fell to a religious of the Order of Mercy, who took as his text: "He that believeth in Me shall live, even after his death."

Reports of wonderful happenings throughout the city were circulated as the hours went on. One in particular seemed most significant.

Soon after Father Pedro had been clothed in the priestly vestments and laid in the handsome shrine, one who wished to publicly express his belief that the dead Apostle was even now in heaven, had been in the act of placing a palm, symbolic of final victory, in his hand, a hand that still remained flexible. As he was doing so the hand opened of itself, received the palm, then closed upon it. This extraordinary circumstance was vouched for by the fathers of the college, city magistrates and others who were present.

The precious relics were reverently interred in the chapel of our Lord, at the epistle side of the altar, in a niche prepared to receive them. So Father Pedro Claver, who had loved lowly things and lowly souls, who had sought to be reckoned the least of men, went to his resting place amidst the prayers and tears of those who had known and revered him, in a triumph accorded only to the Saints.

Chapter XI

IN THE LITTLE HOUSE on the Calle de San Ignacio all the Community knew the heroism and beauty of the soul of him whom they had called their brother in the religious life of the Society of Jesus. Passing up the stairs leading to the empty chamber over the portery they thought of him and begged him to intercede for them with Him whom he had loved "much, very much." In the church Father Claver's confessional was deserted. The Father Superior had put away the small "present" table, a solemn grief-stricken look on his face.

In the chamber where Claver had dwelled for nearly forty years, engaged in the great work of the sanctification of his own soul and the souls of the slaves, only the hide bed remained in its corner. From the wall Brother Alfonso looked down with an eloquent expression in eyes that seemed to guard secrets known only to the heavenly court concerning him so lately gone to its cloisters of rose and pearl.

In the Hospital of San Sebastiano the poor sick fingered the beads and medals given them by their Father in Christ at the most beautiful moment of their lives. Looking about them they remembered that the blessed hands of Father Pedro had carried the rough stones and put them in place in the work of restoration of their partly ruined chapel. They no longer thought of their pain and loss but of the words of him who had assured them that suffering was infinitely desirable since it brought souls close to the Divine Sufferer.

In the Hospital of San Lazaro, outside the walls, the deformed and mutilated lepers gazed wistfully into space as they tried to visualize the lithe figure of their spiritual Father coming toward them. Coming along the Calle de la Media Luna and so to the foot of the low spur of hills that began near that spot and extended to the hill of La Popa. They pictured him eagerly mounting a little ladder, hammer in one hand and a mosquito bar in the other, prepared to do what he could to render their woeful lot a little more bearable. And again they heard him repeating the Divine Praises:

"*Bendito sea Dios! Bendito sea Jesucristo, verdadero Dios y verdadero Hombre!*" "Blessed be God! Blessed be Jesus Christ, true God and true Man!"

As joyously as the young novice, Pedro Claver, had climbed the hill of Tarragona in the long ago, the tired but ever-cheerful Claver had ascended that little ladder in the stifling heat and noisome odors of the charnel house, to erect a barrier between his dear lepers and the pestiferous insects that swarmed about the place.

The sentinels posted in their *guaridas* along the great walls were strangely silent as they peered across the shining expanse over which Pedro Claver had come, four decades before, to this distant kingdom to take men's hearts by storm and win them for his great King.

In the fields of tobacco and sugar cane the black bondsmen fingered the medal hanging about their necks as they remembered the solemn promises made to God in the presence of His faithful servant, their Good Father.

Of all the bruised hearts in Cartagena of the Indies, none was so sorely stricken as that of Doña Isabel d'Urbina.

After her, two others most deeply mourned the loss of their saintly Father and Guide, Doña Carmen de Badajos and the old Negress, Magdalena Mendoza.

Far away, other spots remembered and grieved for the passing of Father Pedro. In the groves of lime and orange of his native Catalonia; in the fields of wheat and maize, did the soft breezes whisper as if to say that he whose feet had once danced so lightly over them was gone from earth forever? About the old Roman monument on the hill of Tarragona did a somber, brooding silence seem to say that he who as an eager novice had so often climbed the steep ascent to sit on those ruined walls with his companions was no more? Did the gate of the old Jesuit College at Majorca moan on its hinges as if it cried out the story of two elect souls whose goings and comings had once been familiar to it — Alfonso, the contemplative, the theologian, the mystic, and the young starry-eyed Pedro, his brother and disciple?

And Barcelona and Sevilla — did their stately promenades and lovely old houses remember and, remembering, deem themselves fortunate to have witnessed even a brief passage of that life of singular holiness and charm?

There must have been many desolate places on the earth because of Father Pedro's going. But none so desolate as his dear Cartagena, Venice of the Caribbean, every feature of which was known to him as the beatings of his own pure heart.

Outwardly, life in the fortressed city of Don Pedro de Heredia would go on as before. True, no hurrying figure with head gracefully inclined and warm lips moving in prayer would pass on the sunny side of the street. No fragile little priest would climb the Baluarte de San Antonio and, descending on the farther side, hasten to the slave ships to minister to the newly arrived blacks.

However, Cartagena still had its Claver, would have

him forever. That is, the mortal part of him. The other part, the fearless loving spirit, would look down from that fairer world of which he had spoken with such loving insistence, and watch over the brave city and its inhabitants.

Through the narrow sandy streets the little water seller would come as of old, crying in musical notes: *"Agua-a-a"* and dancing before the little burro that unwillingly dragged along the blue-painted cart.

Down the Calle de Santo Domingo and the Calle de los Estribos and all the other pleasant ways the barquillero would come with his crisp cakes, his tin vessel bobbing on his back. He would turn at last into the Calle de San Ignacio and, as he passed the residence of the Jesuit Fathers, would pause to remove his wide-brimmed hat as he gazed long and fervently at two windows looking out to sea. Empty windows, where now no eager face strained to watch for the coming of a slave trader from the far African coasts.

The bells . . . they would peal softly, insistently, as of old. From the Monastery of Santa Cruz de la Popa on its pine-mantled slopes; from San Francisco and San Augustino; from Santa Teresa and Santa Clara and all the other bell towers in Cartagena their voices would merge in a grand *Te Deum* for the singular graces and blessings bestowed on a favored soul during forty years.

Often had the golden voices spoken to Father Pedro Claver as he walked on his way to minister to some needy soul.

Now he no longer paid heed to them.

For he was listening to the bells of heaven.

Epilogue

THE NEGRESS, Concepción Villamil, an old slave belonging to Doña Maria de Jesus Navarro, was returning from her daily visit to San Juan de Dios, formerly San Ignacio, in Cartagena.

Concepción's heart was heavy. The sacred temple, long the dwelling place of the Eucharistic Saviour and the shrine of the apostolate of Father Pedro Claver, was now, in the later part of the nineteenth century, a barracks where the soldiers of the revolution were quartered. The fathers of the Society of Jesus, driven from their humble dwelling adjacent to it, were scattered in distant parts.

Lying on the floor in bestial posture, smoking cigarettes, and drinking strong liquor, the revolutionists blasphemed all decent and holy things and vied with one another in the exchange of vicious stories and in shouting evil imprecations at all who entered the venerable precincts. Their uniforms in shocking disarray, these so-called defenders of liberty were hardly as respectable in appearance as the ragged venders of comestibles who in improvised stalls along the aisles wrangled over the price of vegetables and fruits.

Only the horses, noble brutes, tethered to the pillars and eating from troughs placed on the dismantled altars, lent any semblance of dignity to the scene — they alone were innocent of wrong.

At the foot of a column at the epistle side of the high altar stood a small table, covered with a faded cloth. Upon it rested two sheaves of artificial flowers and a little lamp. Each dawn this lamp was replenished with oil by Concepción Villamil, the slave. Braving the insults and taunts of the soldiers, she went up to the little table and poured oil into the lamp, that it might burn brightly through another day.[1]

The aged Negress alone knew why she did this. Why she knelt on the worn-out carpet before the black marble slab in the wall and prayed a long time. . . . Because she was a broken-down bondswoman and because they made use of the flame to light their cigarettes the soldiers did not molest Concepción or interfere with her self-imposed task.

Concepción alone, of all in the church, knew that behind the black marble slab a wondrous treasure reposed, the sacred relics of the Apostle of the Negroes, Father Pedro Claver, of the Society of Jesus. The old woman often shuddered to think what might have occurred long since had these godless men dreamed of its presence! God had wonderfully guarded the holy remains from molestation, having respect for the merits of His faithful servant.

Concepción was very tired as she walked into the open square. She did not, as formerly, look up to the roof of the church to rest her eyes on the symbol of salvation and devoutly cross herself. The cross had been torn down by the rude rabble who were indulging in their shameless orgies inside the hallowed enclosure.

Over the young Republic of Colombia a fratricidal revolution glowed as did the brazen sun, far up in the tropical sky. Throughout the city of Cartagena the profane roll of drums and the blare of trumpets sounded

---

[1] Tradition says that this pious act was performed by the old Negress during seventeen years. The exact date of this incident is not known, but it was probably some time between the years 1861 and 1885.

everywhere; their warlike clarion had displaced the music of the church bells.

Concepción was very tired. But a few stragglers were about in the city, for the gates had only shortly been opened by the watchman, admitting those who had arrived late the night before. The dawn was streaking the eastern horizon with tints of opal and the sun was only beginning to kindle into the great saffron fire that a few hours later would blaze high in the sky.

The Caribbean rocked with gentle motion after a quiet night; the white foam of the waves rubbed against the sea walls as suds in a vast tub, washing it clean of the weeds and mud the surf had thrown up.

The old slave woman sat down beneath a bonga tree to rest her weary bones and fan herself with a branch gathered by the roadside. She closed her heavy-lidded eyes, that she might once more vision the panorama that so often unfolded in her still alert mind. . . .

Her mother had told her much of the venerated Apostle, Father Pedro Claver, the Good Father of the slaves. That mother had in turn received the heritage from her own mother, and Concepción's lady mistress, Doña Maria de Jesus Navarro, had added many touching details to the narrative. It runs as follows.

Because of the many wonderful favors believed to have been wrought through the intercession of Father Claver, from the time of his burial, the Provincial of the Jesuits, Father Gaspar de Cugia, ordered the wall behind which the body rested to be opened and the cedar sarcophagus removed. This was done on March 1, 1657, two years and a half, less eight days, from the time of his burial. An official examination of the remains then took place.

In presence of the entire Jesuit Community, the authorities of Cartagena, and experienced physicians, the proceedings were initiated.

It soon appeared that the excessive humidity of the place had caused grave damage to the sarcophagus, the gift of Doña Isabel d'Urbina to her saintly Father in God. The costly shrine had almost rotted away; its cloth lining had melted into ashes and the gold braid adorning it had also crumbled.

When the coffin was opened, to the surprise and edification of all present, the sacred body was found to be almost intact. Only the head, slightly damaged by the quicklime placed about the remains, had suffered. The flesh of the entire remains preserved all the freshness and vigor of life, so that those who looked on it seemed to be viewing one who had just been placed in the tomb.

The sweet fragrance that had emanated from the holy body a few minutes after Claver's death now exuded from it, filling the chapel.

A warm color suffused the face and hands of Father Pedro; the expression on his countenance was peaceful and gentle as it had been in life.

Doctor Don Bartolomé Torres, one of the medical men named to assist at the ceremony, scrupulously examined all the sacred members. He then declared, in a verbal process, that their condition, so admirably preserved despite the lime that had covered them and the humidity that had penetrated the tomb during nearly three years, was, in his judgment, most astonishing, and in the nature of a miracle.

With the greatest reverence the remains were clothed in new vestments, placed in a new coffin and sarcophagus and returned to their former location. The aperture in the wall was closed up and the seals of the ecclesiastical and civil authorities placed upon it.

In 1660 all the documents concerning the life and works of Father Claver were sent to Rome in order that an infallible verdict might be passed upon them. Countless times these relations were examined as they had been narrated in the Curia of Cartagena. The inquiry into the virtues of the Apostle and the deposition concerning them were made three years after the first exhumation of the remains and their subsequent entombment.

Pope Benedict XIV, with the unanimous consent of all the members of the Sacred Congregation of Rites, in the year 1747 declared "that the virtues of the Venerable Father Claver, Priest and Professed Religious of the Company of Jesus, were singularly heroic and of such grade that with security his cause of canonization might be advanced." Some years before this, in 1719, the Promoter for the Faith in the cause of Father Claver had said that of all the causes then pending he believed this to be the most distinguished and admirable.

The two possible obstacles proposed by the Advocate for the Church as opposed to the heroicity of Claver's virtues were speedily dissolved by the Holy Father, who in a decree given on the twenty-fourth day of September of the year 1747, said:[2]

"Coming to the difficulties proposed, the first is this:

"The Servant of God prayed during the night on his knees in his chamber, the door closed, a rope about his neck and a crown of thorns on his head, his body partially stripped. When the Rector of the college entered, suddenly, in order to confess to him, the Servant of God turned toward him and said: 'What do you want of me? Go away, I beg of you; I am praying.' This might be attributed to a lack of respect for his Superior. But if one examines well the circumstances surrounding this act, he will find in it nothing contrary to the heroicity of Claver's virtues, and, above all, to the respect due his Superior. All that could

---

[2] Author's translation, from the text of Fr. Fleuriau's *La Vie du Vénérable Père Pierre Claver*, afterwards compared with the Latin of the original decree.

be suspected would be at most a little impatience, due to surprise, which was speedily repaired. For, having put on his habit, Claver would go to the Rector's room, throw himself on his knees and beg him, with tears, to leave him in peace; to choose another confessor in view of the fact that there were so many other religious in the college to whom he could make known the state of his conscience. This the Rector did, without difficulty. Here we may apply the inferential proposition contained in our work on the *Canonization of Saints* (Book 3, Chapter 39, number 8). 'That a venial fault of surprise does not hinder true sanctity, especially if one has taken precautions to avoid it . . .' an argument authorized by Saint Ambrose in his apologia on David.

"To this first difficulty succeeds another, founded on the following fact: Although the venerable servant of God, in fulfilling his efforts to deter the Negroes newly converted to the Faith from taking part in the improper dances common to their country; in the fear of seeing them, as often happened, return to their vomit . . . sometimes struck the culprits with a whip and sometimes with a key which he happened to hold in his hand, nevertheless, if one gives serious attention to the character and indolence of the Negroes, to their natural ferocity, to their contempt for the warnings he had given them; if one considers the sweetness of the servant of God, manifested on so many occasions and so many marks of his extreme charity and tenderness toward the Negroes, who always respected him as their benefactor and their Father; if one reflects that never did these strong corrections excite the least complaint against him, one will be unable to find anything to reprehend, anything that opposes this sweetness and the duty of a missionary."

The Pontiff then recalled the admonitions of St. Paul in his Epistles to the Galatians and the Corinthians and to

Titus, in all of which he recommends the necessary severity when sweetness fails to bring the desired reformation of the lives of those meriting the correction.

With these objections cast aside, Pope Benedict XIV solemnly declared that the virtues of the Apostle of Cartagena were heroic in the highest degree, thus paving the way for Claver's beatification and canonization.

In her simple mind, old Concepción Villamil went over these important events in connection with her beloved Good Father. She could not look into the future, as Claver could and often did, and envision events still hidden from ordinary mortals. Her aged heart would have rejoiced with a great joy could she have known that Father Pedro Claver would be elevated to the rank of the Blessed on September 21, 1851, by His Holiness Pope Pius IX. Or that, on the Feast of All Saints, of the year 1887, His Holiness Pope Leo XIII would approve the two miracles proposed for the canonization of the Slave of Slaves (both of these occurred in America). That finally, on January 15, 1888, Pedro Claver would be solemnly canonized in St. Peter's Basilica at Rome amidst a setting of solemn grandeur, on which day his cherished teacher and guide, Brother Alfonso Rodriguez, would also be enrolled among the Saints.

Concepción Villamil rose from her seat under the bonga tree and limped slowly home. She carried the little vessel, now drained of oil, from which she had fed Father Claver's lamp.

She was so very tired. Her heart was heavy in her breast. She could not know that in the not distant future, when the hideous revolution was over and the Jesuits had returned to the city of their Apostle, another servant of the Most High, Bishop Eugenio Biffi, sent from Milan by the Vicar of Christ, would repair the ruins wrought by man and restore the venerable temple, to be known to posterity as San Pedro Claver. Or that with him would come a young

priest, Father Pedro Adan Brioschi, his secretary, to be his
right hand in the work entrusted to him by the Shepherd
of Christendom, as well as the biographer of the Slave of
Slaves . . . a young priest one day to become Cartagena's
first archbishop and the promoter of the cult of the Apostle
of Cartagena.

Of one thing the old Negress was certain. When the
long garish day of her life was ended, she would go forth
on feet strangely young and swift, bearing in her hand a
little lamp, brightly burning, to be welcomed by the Good
Father of the Slaves.

Beneath the high altar in the Church of San Pedro Claver,
Cartagena, in an urn supported by two gilt angels, rest the
mortal remains of the noble Apostle who is believed to
have baptized three hundred thousand negro slaves during
his glorious apostolate. Only the skull of the Saint is visible,
*"Aquella santa cabeza que fue la sede de tantos pensami-
entos y aspiraciones sublimes,"* "That holy head which was
the seat of so many sublime thoughts and aspirations," as
Father Mejia exclaims in his *Life* of the Apostle. The major
part of the relics now in existence are composed beneath
a white and gold chasuble, the gift of His Eminence Cardinal Miecislaus Ledochowski, Relator of the Cause of
Father Claver, to one whom he deeply reverenced and
admired.

When the urn was opened, in 1851, at the time of Claver's
beatification, the two hip bones and thigh bones were ex-
tracted; one set was sent to Rome, the other retained by
the Bishop of Cartagena.

Let us suppose that, accompanied by a member of the
Community of San Pedro Claver, you have just come from
the little room above the portery in the adjacent college,
"perfumed by the heroic virtues of Claver for forty years,"
and definitely established as his chamber by the finding of a

stone slab close to the outer wall, bearing the inscription: "In this room the Venerable Father Pedro Claver died, the eighth day of September, 1654." Now you are privileged to kneel on the top altar step, close to the treasured relics, seen through a glass panel, after the shrine containing the urn has been opened.

As Pére L'Hande experienced in the presence of the mortal remains of St. Francis Xavier, you recognize that the sacred skull, particularly the forehead, presents an aspect "indescribably living." The bone structure, resembling highly polished yellow or light brown wood, of satiny sheen, reflects the serenity and patience that characterized the life of the Slave of the Slaves.

In the historic church, restored to the fathers of the Society of Jesus after one hundred years of exile, a solemn sadness seems to linger, as if it could not forget the long years of desecration and neglect. At the foot of this altar, over fifty years ago, the then young secretary of Bishop Eugenio Biffi, Father Pedro Adan Brioschi, conceived the thought of writing the life of the Saint of Cartagena. . . .

"Prostrate before the sacred tomb which enshrines the relics of St. Peter Claver," he says, "we were one day supplicating the illustrious Apostle to give us strength from heaven to fulfill the heavy burdens of our sublime office of 'anointed of the Lord' when, for the first time we experienced an unwonted and heavy sadness. We knew not how to explain this, for always when we had visited the sepulchre of the Saint our soul had been inundated with a sweet and happy emotion.

"Contemplating the venerated tomb and the deserted temple which safeguards the incalculable treasure . . . we seemed to hear an interior voice, saying: 'Why do not more of the faithful come to visit the Father of the Poor?' "[*]

[*] From the preface of the *Vida De San Pedro Claver*.

So the *Vida De San Pedro Claver* was written by that young priest who, as Chief Shepherd of the Archdiocese of Cartagena, today holds the key to the urn containing the relics of the Saint.

Outside, across the sparkling Caribbean, the great ships come and go. They bring tourists who remain for a few hours in the favored city, then sail on to other ports. But few of these are pilgrims, for St. Peter Claver's shrine is little known and visited by any from outside his adopted country.

Reluctantly you turn from the spot forever endeared to holiest recollection. You pass through the aged corridors into the patio where the sun is gilding the tall palms in the waning of the day. The grilled door is opened and you enter the plaza where hundreds of St. Peter Claver's "children" have gathered to smile upon you and bid you: *Adios!*

As you look back two white-robed figures are watching, their hands uplifted in blessing. The one is a young Colombian Jesuit whose invaluable assistance made possible the writing of this book; the other is a venerable spiritual brother of the Apostle, an exile from his native Spain where his sister, a nun, was martyred by the Reds a few years before.

With Pére L'Hande, in the realization of his own great desire, one thought remains with you . . .

"Blessed are the eyes that see the things that you see."